# THE CONQUEST

# OF DEATH

# JOHN MIDDLETON MURRY

*Constant*

# THE CONQUEST
# OF DEATH

## PETER NEVILL LIMITED
London      New York

PETER NEVILL LIMITED
50 Old Brompton Road
London SW7 and
122 East 55th Street, New
York 22          NY

Printed    in    Great    Britain    by
Hamilton    Publications
Burnley   -   Lancashire
M C M L I

# CONTENTS

5

# PREFACE

This book is a consideration of the problem of love and death, which is the fundamental problem of human life, and therefore of religion. It has a peculiar form. The first part of it is a translation of Benjamin Constant's *Adolphe*: the second part is a commentary and meditation upon that story, which by common consent is a masterpiece.

I could not dispense with the necessity of making and printing a translation of *Adolphe*. What I have to say about it required that it should be fresh in the reader's mind, and that he could refer back to it continually. For the most important fact about *Adolphe*, from my point of view, is that it is, or contains, a " revelation," in the religious sense of the word. It is not much use talking about a " revelation " at one or two removes. It needs to be exhibited. This book is both a meditation on the problem of love and death, and an assertation of the reality of " revelation." To assert the reality of " revelation " is futile, unless one can say, " Here it is !"

The translation of *Adolphe* was therefore necessary in order that I could say to my reader " Here it is !" If he does not experience the " revelation," then what I try to say about it will be so much nonsense to him. But if, as I hope, he does experience it, he will find some meaning in what I try to say.

7

# PART I

## EDITOR'S FOREWORD

Many years ago I was travelling in Italy. I was held up in an inn at Cerenza, a little village in Calabria, by a flood of the river Neto. In the same inn, for the same reason, was a stranger. He was very silent and sad-looking; he showed no sign of impatience. He was the only man I could speak to in the place, and I sometimes complained to him of the delay in our journey. " It is all the same to me," he replied, " whether I am here or elsewhere."

The landlord, who had talked to the Neapolitan servant who attended him, but did not know his name, told me that he did not travel from curiosity : for he visited neither ruins nor sites, nor monuments, nor men. He read a great deal, but desultorily; he went for walks in the evening, always alone, and often he spent whole days sitting motionless, with his head in his hands.

Just when the roads were open again, and we could have resumed our journey, the stranger fell seriously ill. I felt it my duty to stay to look after him. There was only a village-surgeon at Cerenza. I wanted to send to Cosenza for more effective help. " It is not worth it," said the stranger. " The man here is exactly what I need." He was right, perhaps more than he thought—for the man cured him. " I did not think you were so clever," he said to him rather crossly when he dismissed

Some months later at Naples I received a letter from the landlord at Cerenza, together with a despatch-box which had been found on the road to Strongoli. The stranger and I had both gone by this road—but separately. The inn-keeper who sent the box was sure it belonged to one of us. It contained a number of very old letters either without addresses, or with the addresses and signatures erased, a woman's portrait, and a notebook containing the anecdote or history that follows. The stranger to whom these things belonged had left me no means of writing to him when we parted. I kept them for ten years, not knowing what to do with them. One day, I happened to speak of them to some people in a German town; and one of them pressed me to lend him the manuscript. A week later, it was returned to me with a letter which I have printed at the end of the narrative, because it would be unintelligible to anyone reading it without having read the story itself.

This letter made me decide to publish, for it assured me that no-one would be offended or compromised by publication. I have not changed a word in the original: I am not even responsible for the suppression of the names; they were distinguished, as they are now, only by initials.

# CHAPTER I

At twenty-two I had just finished my studies at the University of Göttingen. My father, who was Minister of State to the Elector of ————, intended me to travel through the most interesting countries of Europe and then to join him in his department of State. There he would train me to take his place one day. In spite of an irregular life, by fairly pertinacious work I had achieved successes which distinguished me from my fellow-students, and aroused in my father hopes of me which were probably exaggerated.

These hopes had made him indulgent towards many of my extravagances. He had never left me to suffer their consequences. He always granted and sometimes anticipated my demands.

Unfortunately his conduct towards me was noble and generous rather than tender. I was deeply sensible of all his claims to my gratitude and my respect; but there had never been any mutual confidence between us. There was an ironical tinge in him which agreed badly with my character. At that time I wanted only to surrender myself to those primitive and passionate feelings which lift the soul out of the common sphere and fill it with disdain for its surroundings. I found my father no censor indeed, but a cold and caustic

13

observer who first smiled pityingly, and then impatiently ended the conversation. For the first eighteen years of my life I cannot remember our ever talking together for an hour. His letters were affectionate, full of reasonable and sensitive advice; but no sooner were we in each other's presence than something constrained appeared in him which I could not account for and which had a distressing effect upon me. At that time I did not know the nature of shyness—the inward suffering which pursues us even into old age, thrusts our deepest feelings back into our own heart, freezes our speech, denatures on our very lips all that we are trying to say, and allows us to express ourselves only by vague words and a rather bitter irony, as though we wanted to take revenge on our feelings for our pain at being unable to communicate them. I did not know that my father was shy even with his son, and that often after long waiting for some signs of affection which his apparent coldness seemed to forbid, he left me with tears in his eyes and sadly said to others that I did not love him.

My constraint with him had a great influence on my character. As shy as he, but less controlled, because I was younger, I grew accustomed to keep all my experiences to myself. I made only solitary plans, counted only on myself for their execution, and considered the advice, the interest, the help and even the presence of others as an irritant and an obstacle. I formed the habit of never speaking of my concerns, of submitting to conversation only as a tiresome necessity, and of enlivening it by a perpetual levity which made it less fatiguing to me and helped me to hide my real thoughts. From this grew a lack of spontaneity with which my friends reproach me even now, and a disinclination to talk seriously which it is still hard to overcome. At the same time it created in me a passionate desire for independence, a consuming impatience of the connections which surrounded me, and an invincible terror of forming new ones. I was at my ease only when alone; and such is the effect of this disposition, even now, that if I have to make a choice, even in the most trivial circumstances, I am embarrassed by a human presence, and my instinctive movement is to escape in order to think it over in peace.

Nevertheless, I was not so utterly egotistic as this description suggests: although I was interested only in myself, my interest in myself was faint. Deep in my heart was a craving for tenderness of which I was unaware, but which, finding no satisfaction, drew me away from the succession of things which attracted my curiosity. This indifference to everything was strengthened by the idea of death—an idea which had impressed me at a very early age, and men's insensitiveness to which has

always been incomprehensible to me. When
I was seventeen, I witnessed the death of an
older woman whose distinguished and unusual
mind had begun to develop my own. She, like
many others, at the beginning of her career,
had entered society, with which she was unfamiliar, with the consciousness of a great
force of soul and truly powerful faculties; also,
like many others, because she did not submit
to its artificial but necessary conventions, she
had seen her hopes deceived, and her youth
pass without happiness. Old age overtook
her at last but could not subdue her. She
lived in a château near one of our estates,
retired and discontented; her mind was her
only resource, and with her mind she analysed
everything. For nearly a year, in our unending conversations, we reviewed life in all
its aspects, with death always as the end of all.
After talking of death so much with her, I
saw death strike her before my eyes.

That experience filled me with a feeling of
uncertainty about human destiny, and a vague
dreaminess which never left me. The poetry
I read for preference was that which recalled
the brevity of human life. I decided that no
goal was worth the price of the effort. It is
curious that this persuasion has diminished
precisely as my years have grown. Can it be
because there is something doubtful in hope,
and that when it withdraws, a man's career
takes on a severer but more positive character?

Because life seems more real when all illusions disappear, just as the peak and the rocks of a mountain are more clearly outlined against the horizon when the clouds dissolve.

When I left Göttingen, I went to the little city of ———. It was the capital of a prince who, like most of those in Germany, mildly governed a small dominion, protected the enlightened men who came to live there, and allowed complete liberty to all opinions; but, limited by tradition to the society of his courtiers, gathered round him men for the most part mediocre and insignificant. I was welcomed into this court with the curiosity which greets every stranger who comes to break the circle of monotony and etiquette. For several months I saw nothing to captivate my attention. I was grateful for the politeness shown to me; but either my shyness prevented me from taking advantage of it, or the fatigue of aimless activity made me prefer solitude to the insipid pleasures I was invited to share. I did not hate anybody, but few aroused my interest. Men are offended by indifference, which they attribute to ill-will or affectation; they refuse to believe that it may be natural to be bored by their company. Sometimes I tried to suppress my boredom, by taking refuge in silence; the silence was taken for disdain. At other times, tired of my own taciturnity, I plunged into pleasantry, and my wit, once set in motion, carried me to excess. In a day I revealed all the subjects for laughter I had observed in a month. The recipients of my sudden and involuntary expansiveness did not thank me for it; and they were right; for it was the need to speak that seized me—not the need to confide.

In my conversations with the lady who had first drawn out my mind, I had acquired an unconquerable aversion to all common maxims and all dogmatic formulas. When I listened to mediocrity complacently expatiating on established and incontrovertible principles of morality, polite behaviour or religion —all which it cheerfully puts on the same plane —I felt impelled to contradict, not because I held the opposite opinions, but because such positive and ponderous conviction irritated me. Besides, an instinct warned me to distrust these general axioms, devoid of qualification and innocent of nuance. Fools make a compact and indivisible mass of their morality, so that it shall mix as little as possible with their actions and leave them free in all the details.

By this behaviour I soon acquired a great reputation for levity, persiflage and maliciousness. My bitter speeches were considered proofs of a spiteful soul, my witticisms an affront to all that is respectable. Those whom I was misguided enough to laugh at conveniently identified themselves with the principles which they accused me of undermining. Because I had unintentionally made them laugh at one another's expense, they all united against me. They seemed to think that in revealing their foibles I had betrayed a confidence they had reposed in me, and that in showing me their characters, they had obtained a promise of silence from me: I was completely unconscious of having accepted so one-sided an agreement. They had found pleasure in letting themselves go, I found it in observing and describing them. What they called a betrayal, I considered an innocent and legitimate compensation.

I do not wish to justify myself; besides I have long given up this frivolous and facile trick of inexperience. I only wish to say on behalf of others than myself (who am now retired from society) that it takes time to grow accustomed to human kind as it has been shaped by interest, affectation, vanity and fear. The astonishment of youth at the aspect of a society so artificial and so elaborate is the sign of a natural heart more than a wicked mind. Besides, society has nothing to fear from it; society presses so hard upon us, its dumb influence is so powerful, that it soon shapes us into the universal mould. Then our former surprise alone surprises us, and we are comfortable in our new form, just as one is stifled on entering a crowded theatre, yet ends by breathing freely there.

If some people escape from this common

destiny, they keep their secret nonconformity
to themselves; they perceive in most absurdi-
ties the germ of vices; but they do not jest
about them, because contempt replaces mock-
ery, and contempt is silent.

Thus the small society which surrounded
me came to feel a vague uneasiness about my
character. They could not point to any evil
action of mine; they could not even deny that
I had done one or two which seemed to indicate generosity or devotion; but they said that
I was unprincipled and unreliable: two epithets
happily invented to insinuate the unknown.

# CHAPTER II

Distrait, unwary and bored, I was quite unconscious of the impression I was making. My time was divided between studies which I often interrupted, plans I did not carry out and pleasures which hardly interested me, when a circumstance, apparently trifling, produced an important revolution in my disposition.

I was fairly intimate with a young man who had been trying for some months to find favour in the eyes of one of the least insipid women in our society; and I was the disinterested confidant of his enterprise. After long efforts he succeeded in making himself loved; as he had not concealed his reverses and his griefs, he felt obliged to tell me of his success; he was transported with joy. The spectacle of such happiness made me regret that I had never yet tried it for myself. Up to that time I had no liaison with a woman which could flatter my self-esteem. A new future seemed to open before me, I felt a new craving arise in the depths of my heart. No doubt there was a good deal of vanity in this craving, but it was not only vanity; and perhaps there was less than I myself believed. A man's sentiments are confused and mixed; they are composed of a multitude of various feelings which cannot be observed. Words, always too clumsy and too general, may serve to indicate them; but they can never define them.

In my father's house, I had adopted a pretty immoral code about women. Although he strictly observed the outward proprieties, my father frequently spoke lightly of liaisons; he looked upon them as amusements, if not permitted, at least excusable; marriage alone was to be taken seriously. His principle in the matter was that a young man must carefully avoid what is called a folly: that is, contracting a permanent engagement with a woman who was not entirely his equal in fortune, birth and external advantages. For the rest, provided there was no question of marrying them, all women could be taken and left with equanimity. I have seen him smile, with a sort of approval, at this parody of a well-known mot: " It does them so little harm, and gives us so much pleasure!"

Men do not realise what a profound impression worldly wisdom of that kind makes on early youth, or how astounded children are, at an age when all their opinion are still doubtful and wavering, to see the plain rules they have been given contradicted by pleasantries that everyone applauds. For them, immediately, the rules become banal formulas which their parents are in league to repeat to them to salve their conscience, and the pleasantries seem to contain the veritable secret of life.

Troubled by a vague emotion, I said to myself: " I want to be loved," and I looked around me. I saw no one who inspired love in me, or whom I thought capable of feeling it; I examined my heart and inclinations, and I felt no motion of preference. While I was in this inward agitation, I made the acquaintance of Count P——— a man of forty, whose family was connected with mine. He invited me to go and see him. Ill-fated visit! He had with him his mistress, a Polish lady, famous for her beauty, though she was no longer young. In spite of her compromising position, she had shown, on several occasions, the distinction of her character. Her family, rather illustrious in Poland, had been ruined in that country's vicissitudes. Her father had been banished, her mother had fled to France, and taken her daughter with her. There the mother died, leaving her daughter completely isolated. Count P——— had fallen in love with her. I never learned the beginnings of the liaison which, when I first saw Ellenore, was long established and, so to speak, consecrated. Had the fatality of her situation, or the inexperience of her youth, thrown her into a life repugnant alike to her education, her habits, and the pride which was so remarkable in her character? What I know, what everybody knew, is that the fortune of Count P——— had been almost entirely ruined and his freedom in danger, and that Ellenore had given him such proofs of devotion, so scornfully rejected the most brilliant offers, had shared his dangers and his poverty with such eagerness and even joy, that the most scrupulous severity was constrained to do justice to the purity of her motives and the disinterestedness of her conduct. To her activity, her courage, her good sense, to the sacrifices of every kind which she had borne uncomplainingly, her lover owed the recovery of a portion of his wealth. They had come to live in D——— to attend to a law-suit by which Count P——— might recover all his former wealth, and they reckoned on staying there about two years.

Ellenore's intellect was not extraordinary; but her ideas were just, and her simple expression of them was sometimes striking because of the nobility and elevation of her feelings. She had a number of prejudices; but they were all opposed to her interest. She set the highest value on regularity of conduct, precisely because her own was irregular by conventional standards. She was very religious, because religion rigorously condemned her mode of life. In conversation she severely rejected what other women would have considered innocent pleasantries, because she was always afraid that her situation might be thought to justify pleasantries of another sort being addressed to her. She would have liked to receive only men of the highest rank and the most exemplary morals, because the kind of women to whom she shuddered to be compared ordinarily form a mixed society for themselves: they are resigned to their loss of consideration, and look only for amusement in their social relations.  In short, Ellenore was constantly struggling against her destiny.  By her every action and word she protested against the class she was ranked in.  Since she felt that reality was stronger than she, and that her efforts changed nothing in the situation, she was very unhappy.  She brought up the two children she had borne to Count P——— with an excessive austerity.  Her attachment to them was more passionate than tender, and one sometimes suspected in it a secret revolt which made them somehow irksome.  Well-meant remarks on how her children were growing, on the promise they showed, on their future careers, made her pale at the thought that one day she must tell them of their birth.  But the least danger, or an hour's absence brought her back to them with an anxiety in which one detected a tinge of remorse and a longing to give them by her caresses the happiness which caresses had not given to her.

This conflict between her sentiments and the place she held in society had made her moods very variable.  Often she was dreamy and silent; sometimes she burst into a flood of speech.  Tormented by one particular thought, in the most general conversation she never remained perfectly calm.  But by that very fact there was something passionate and unexpected in her manner which made it more intriguing than it would have been otherwise. The peculiarity of her situation took the place of novelty in her ideas. She aroused curiosity and interest like a beautiful storm.

Coming before me at a moment when my heart craved for love and my vanity for success, Ellenore appeared a conquest worthy of me. She herself found pleasure in the society of a man different from those she had seen before. Her circle was composed of a few friends and relations of her lover, and their wives, whom Count P———'s influence had compelled to recognise his mistress. The husbands had neither feelings nor ideas; the wives differed from their husbands only in that their mediocrity was more uneasy and nervous because they lacked the tranquillity which comes from being regularly occupied with business. A lighter vein, a more varied conversation, a peculiar blend of melancholy and gaiety, of despondency and interest, of enthusiasm and irony, astonished and attracted Ellenore. She spoke several languages, not very correctly, but always with vivacity and sometimes with grace. Her ideas seemed to emerge into the light through obstacles, and the struggle made them more agreeable, more naive, and more original; for thoughts are rejuvenated by a foreign idiom; it cleanses them from turns of expression which make them appear either commonplace or affected. We read the English poets together; we went for walks. I often went to see her in the morning: we talked on every subject under the sun.

My intention was to make a complete review of her character and mind as a cool and impartial observer; but every word she spoke to me seemed clothed in an inexplicable grace. My purpose of attracting her put a new interest in my life and gave an unfamiliar animation to my existence. This almost magical effect I attributed to her charm; I should have enjoyed it even more completely but for my engagement to my self-esteem. This self-esteem made a third between Ellenore and me. I felt myself obliged to reach my goal as quickly as possible; and so I did not give myself up unreservedly to my feelings. I was impatient to speak the word, because I thought I had only to speak it to succeed. I did not believe I loved Ellenore; but by now it would have been unbearable to me to fail to please her. She occupied my mind incessantly; I made plans innumerable; I invented innumerable modes of conquest with the ignorant fatuity which believes itself sure of success because it has never made the attempt.

Nevertheless, an invincible shyness held me back: all my speeches died on my lips, or ended quite differently from my plans. I struggled inwardly; I was indignant with myself.

Finally I looked for an argument to extricate me from this struggle with honour in my own eyes. I said to myself that things must not be rushed, that Ellenore was not sufficiently prepared for the declaration I was contemplating, and that it was better to wait longer. Almost always, to live at peace with ourselves, we transform our incapacities and weaknesses into calculations and philosophies: that satisfies the part of ourselves which looks on at the other.

This situation dragged on. Every day, I fixed to-morrow as the certain date of a positive declaration, and every to-morrow passed like yesterday. My shyness left me as soon as I left Ellenore; I then returned to my clever plans and my subtle strategies: but no sooner was I in her presence than I was troubled and trembling again. Anyone reading my heart, while I was away from her, would have taken me for a cold and unfeeling seducer; anyone seeing me at her side would have seen in me a novice lover, tongue-tied and passionate. Both judgments would have been equally mistaken: there is no entire unity in man, and he is hardly ever completely sincere, or completely false.

These repeated experiences convinced me that I should never have the courage to speak to Ellenore, and I made up my mind to write to her. Count P——— was away. My long struggle with my own character, my impatience at not being able to overcome it, my uncertainty about the success of my attempt, lent my letter an agitation which was very like love. Besides, I was fired by my own writing and, as I finished the letter, I felt a touch of the passion I had tried to express as frankly as I could.

Ellenore saw in my letter what was natural to see in it—the transient transport of a man ten years younger than herself, whose heart was budding into feelings hitherto unknown, and who deserved more pity than anger. She replied kindly, gave me affectionate advice, offered me her sincere friendship, but told me that she could not see me again until Count P——— had returned.

The answer shattered me. My imagination, inflamed by the obstacle, seized hold of me completely. An hour before I had been congratulating myself on my pretence of love; suddenly I seemed to experience the fury of its reality. I rushed to Ellenore; I was told she was out. I wrote to her; I implored her to grant me a last interview; in pitiful terms, I depicted my despair, and the fatal projects with which her cruel decision had inspired me. For most of the day, I waited for her answer in vain. I calmed my unspeakable suffering only by repeating that to-morrow I would brave all difficulties and get to Ellenore and speak to her. In the evening I received a few words from her: they were gentle. I thought I could detect in them a tinge of regret and sadness; but she persisted in her resolve, which she said was unshakable. I went to her house again the next day. She had gone to a country house; her servants did not know its name. They had no means even of sending letters on.

For a long time I stood motionless at her door, seeing no chance of finding her again. I myself was astonished at what I was suffering. My memory recalled the moments when I had told myself that I aspired only to a conquest; that it was only an attempt which I could easily abandon. I had never dreamed of the violent, uncontrollable pain which now seized my heart. I was incapable alike of study and distraction. I wandered incessantly near Ellenore's house. I walked up and down the city as though at every turn of the street I might hope to meet her. One morning during one of these aimless wanderings which served to replace my agitation by fatigue, I saw Count P———'s carriage: he was returning from his journey. He recognised me, and got out. I disguised my emotion, and after a few banal phrases, I spoke of Ellenore's sudden departure. " Yes," he said, " one of her friends, some miles from here, is in some trouble or other, and Ellenore thought that she could help and console her. She went off without consulting me. She is always at the mercy of her feelings; her soul is always in a ferment, and finds a sort of rest in self-devotion. But I need her here too badly. I shall write to her.

She will certainly be back in a few days."

The assurance calmed me; I felt my pain assuage. For the first time since Ellenore had gone, I could breathe easily. She did not return as quickly as Count P———— hoped. But I had resumed my normal life and my anguish had begun to dissolve when, a month later, Count P———— sent me word that she would arrive that evening. As he was eager to keep her the place in society which her character deserved, but her situation forbade, he had invited to supper some of his female relatives and women-friends who were willing to meet her.

My memories revived, at first confused, then more vivid. My self-esteem was involved with them. I was embarrassed and humiliated at meeting a woman who had treated me as a child. I seemed to see her at my approach, smiling at the thought that a brief absence had calmed the effervescence of a young head; and in the smile I sensed a sort of contempt for me. Gradually, my sentiments came to life again. That very day I had waked without a thought of Ellenore; an hour after the news of her return, her image swam before my eyes, ruled my heart, and I was feverish with the fear of not seeing her.

I stayed at home all day; I kept myself hidden, as it were; I trembled lest the least movement should endanger our meeting. Yet nothing was simpler, or more certain; but I longed for it so ardently that it seemed impossible. Impatience devoured me! I looked incessantly at my watch. I had to open the window to breathe; the blood in my veins was burning.

At last the hour struck when I had to go to the Count's house. Straightway my impatience changed to timidity. I dressed slowly; I was no longer in a fever to get there: I was so terrified lest my expectation should be deceived, and so vividly anticipated the pain I was risking, that I would gladly have postponed it all.

It was pretty late when I entered the house. I saw Ellenore sitting at the end of the room; I dared not move towards her, I felt that everybody was staring at me. I hid myself in a corner of the drawing-room, behind a group of men who were talking. From there I watched Ellenore: she seemed slightly changed, paler than usual. The Count unearthed me from my hiding-place. He came to me, took me by the hand, and led me to her. " Allow me," he said, smiling, " to present one of the men most astonished by your sudden departure." Ellenore was speaking to a lady beside her. When she saw me, her words expired on her lips; she was quite tongue-tied. So almost was I.

We could be heard. I asked her some indifferent questions. We both resumed an appearance of calm. Supper was anounced; I offered Ellenore my arm, which she could not refuse. As I took her in, I said to her: " If you do not promise to receive me at eleven to-morrow morning, I shall go away instantly, abandon my country, my family and my father, break off all my connections, repudiate all my duties, and go anywhere, to end as quickly as I can a life which you are pleased to poison." " Adolphe!" she replied, and hesitated. I started away. I do not know what my face expressed, but I had never felt a spasm so violent. Ellenore looked at me. There was fear, and affection, in her face. " I will see you to-morrow," she said, " but I implore you . . ." There were many people behind us and she could not finish her phrase. I pressed her hand with my arm; we sat down to the table.

I wanted to sit beside Ellenore, but the master of the house had decided otherwise. I was placed nearly opposite. At the beginning of supper she was dreamy. When she was addressed, she replied gently; but she soon relapsed into distraction. One of her friends, struck by her silence and low spirits, asked her if she was unwell. " I have not been very well lately," she replied, " and I am still very shaken." I longed to make an agreeable impression on Ellenore; by showing myself amiable and intelligent, I wanted to dispose her favourably towards me, and prepare her for the interview she had granted me. I tried everything therefore to fix her attention. I

brought the conversation back to subjects in
which, I knew, she was interested; those near
us joined in; I was inspired by her presence;
I succeeded in making her listen to me, and
soon I saw her smile: this filled me with such
joy, there was such gratitude in my eyes, that
she could not help being touched. Her sadness and distraction vanished; she no longer
resisted the secret charm which her soul
received from the sight of the happiness I owed
to her; and when we rose from the table, our
hearts were in sympathy as though we had
never been separated. "You see," I said to
her as I gave her my arm to return to the
salon, "that you are the arbiter of my whole
existence. What have I done that you should
find pleasure in torturing it?"

# CHAPTER III

I passed a sleepless night. There were no more calculations or plans; with the best faith in the world I felt myself truly in love. It was no longer the hope of conquest which impelled me; I was dominated by one thing alone—the craving to see the woman I loved and to enjoy her presence. Eleven o'clock struck; I went to her; she was waiting for me. She wished to speak; I asked her to listen. I sat beside her, for in truth I could hardly stand, and spoke in snatches.

"I have not come to protest against the sentence you have pronounced upon me; I have not come to retract an avowal which may have offended you; I could not, even if I would. This love you reject is indestructible; the effort I am making at this moment to speak to you with some composure is a proof of the violence of the sentiment which wounds you. But I have not asked you to hear me talk about that. On the contrary, it is to ask you to forget it, to receive me as you used to do, to put away the memory of a moment of madness, not to punish me because you know a secret which I should have kept hidden in my inmost soul. You know my situation—what they call my eccentric and uncivilised character, my heart alien to all worldly interests and solitary in the midst of society—a heart which suffers nevertheless from the isolation to which it is

condemned.   Your friendship supported me;
without it I cannot live.   I have formed the
habit of seeing you; you let this precious habit
take root and grow.   What have I done to lose
this solitary consolation of my sad and sombre
existence?   I am horribly unhappy; I have no
more courage to bear an unhappiness which
has lasted so long.   I have no hopes, I make no
demands, I want only to see you; but see you
I must, if I am to live."

Ellenore kept silence.

"What are you afraid of?" I went on.
"What is it that I ask?   What you allow to
anyone who is indifferent to you.   Is it society
you fear?   This society, absorbed by its solemn
frivolities, will never read a heart like mine.
How can I be imprudent, when my life is at
stake?   Ellenore, grant my prayer!   You will
find some sweetness in doing so.   You will
find some charm in being loved like this, in
seeing me near you, occupied only by you,
existing for you alone, owing every feeling of
happiness of which I am still capable to you,
rescued by your presence from misery and
despair."

In this fashion I went on for a long while,
meeting all objections, reshaping every argument that pleaded for me.   I was so submissive,
so resigned; I asked for so little, I should have
been made so unhappy had she refused!

Ellenore was touched.   She imposed
several conditions.   She would receive me

only rarely, and only when others were there, and I must promise never to speak to her of love. I promised everything. We were both content: I, at having regained the precious thing I had nearly lost, she, at being generous, tender-hearted, and prudent all at the same time.

The very next day I availed myself of my permission; and the following days. Ellenore thought no more of the necessity that my visits should be seldom: soon nothing seemed simpler than that she should see me every day. Ten years' fidelity had inspired Count P——— with utter confidence; Ellenore's freedom was entire. Since he had had to struggle against the attempt to exclude his mistress from the society in which he had to live, he was happy to see her circle grow. A house full of visitors was his triumph over opinion.

Whenever I arrived, I saw pleasure in Ellenore's eyes. When the conversation amused her, they turned instinctively to me. There was no interesting story told but I was called to hear it. But she was never alone: whole evenings passed without my being able to say anything particular to her—only a few insignificant or interrupted words. It was not long before I was irritated by this constraint. I became sombre and reserved; my temper variable, my conversation bitter. I could hardly contain myself when somebody else spoke tête-à-tête with her; I brusquely interrupted. I did not care if people were offended, and I was not always checked by the fear of compromising her. She complained of my change.

" What do you expect?" I said impatiently. " No doubt you think you have done much for me. I cannot help saying you are mistaken. I do not understand your new mode of life. Formerly you lived retired; you fled from wearisome society; you avoided these eternal conversations which go on precisely because they ought never have begun. Nowadays, your door is open to the whole world. One would say that, in asking you to receive me, I have obtained the same favour for the entire universe. I confess that when I used to see you so prudent I hardly expected to find you so frivolous."

I caught on Ellenore's face an expression of displeasure and sadness. I suddenly softened and said:

" Dear Ellenore, haven't I deserved to be distinguished from the tiresome crowd who besiege you? Has not friendship its secrets? Is it not distrustful and shy in the noise and the crowd?

Ellenore feared, if she was unyielding, a return of the imprudences that had alarmed her for herself and me. The idea of breaking with me no longer entered her heart. She agreed to receive me sometimes alone.

Then the strict rules she had imposed upon

me were quickly relaxed. She let me tell of my love; gradually she grew accustomed to this language; soon after she confessed that she loved me.

I passed several hours at her feet, saying that I was the happiest of men, giving her countless assurances of tenderness, devotion and eternal reverence. She told me how she had suffered in trying to keep away from me; how often she had hoped that I would discover her in spite of herself; how the least noise she heard was perhaps my arrival; what emotion, what joy, what fear she had felt at seeing me again; how mistrust of herself had made her try to reconcile the inclination of her heart with prudence, and give herself up to the distractions of society, seeking the crowd she used to flee. I made her repeat the tiniest details, and the history of those few weeks seemed to us the history of a whole life. Love supplies the place of years of memories by a sort of magic. All other affections have need of the past; love creates, by an enchantment, a past to surround us. It gives us the consciousness of having lived for years with a being who was almost a stranger till a little while ago. Love is only a luminous point; nevertheless, it seems to take possession of time. A little while and it did not exist; a little while, and it will exist no more; but, while it exists, it spreads its splendour over the period which preceded it, and over that to come.

But this calm was brief. Ellenore was the more on guard against her weakness, because she was haunted by the memory of her lapses. My imagination, my desires, and a theory of manliness which I myself was unconscious of holding revolted against such a love. Always shy, often irritated, I complained, I lost control, I heaped reproaches on Ellenore. More than once she planned to break off a relation which only disquieted and troubled her life; as often I pacified her by my supplications, my disavowals and my tears.

One day I wrote to her: "Ellenore, you do not know all I suffer. Beside you, away from you, I am equally unhappy. All the time we are apart, I wander about aimlessly, bent under the burden of an existence I do not know how to bear. Society irritates me, solitude crushes me. These nobodies who watch me, who know nothing of what engrosses me, who look at me with curiosity yet without interest, with astonishment yet without pity, who dare to speak to me of other things than you, wound me to death. I run away from them; but, when I am alone, I gasp for air to relieve my breast—in vain. I throw myself on the earth which should open and swallow me; I put my head on the cold stone to calm the burning fever which devours me. I drag myself to the hill which overlooks your house; and there I remain, my eyes fixed on the home where I shall never live with you. If I had met you earlier, you could have been mine! I would have clasped in my arms the only creature formed by Nature for my heart, the heart which has suffered so much because it was looking for you, and because it found you only too late!

When at last these hours of madness end, and the moment arrives when I can see you, I set off trembling for your house. I fear that everyone who meets me will divine my feelings; I stop; I walk slowly; I delay the instant of happiness, the happiness that everything threatens, and I always think I am just about to lose; partial and troubled happiness —for perhaps at every minute fearful events and jealous eyes, tyrannical caprice and your own will, are conspiring against it! When I set foot on your threshold, and begin to open your door, a new terror seizes me: I step forward like a guilty thing, asking pardon of everything I see, as though it were my enemy, and grudged me the hour of felicity I am to enjoy once more. The smallest sound frightens me, the least movement around terrifies me, the very noise of my footsteps makes me start back. Even when I am quite near you I still fear some sudden obstacle may arise between you and me.

At last I see you; I see you and breathe; I look at you and stop short, like a refugee touching the earth of the country that will save him from death. But even then when my whole being leaps towards you, when my craving is to rest after so much anguish, to lay my head on your lap and let my tears flow freely, I must restrain myself by force, and even beside you live a life of effort still. Not a moment's unburdening! Not a moment's abandon! Your eyes watch me. You are embarrassed, offended almost, by my distress. A strange constraint has followed the lovely time when at least you avowed your love. The time flies, new interests summon you: you never forget them; you never delay the moment of my going. Strangers come: now I must not look at you: I feel I must run away to escape the suspicions which surround me. When I leave you, I am more agitated, more torn, madder than I was before; I leave you, and I fall back into that fearful isolation, in which I struggle against myself and never meet a single being on whom I can lean and rest for a moment."

Ellenore had never been loved like this. Count P——— had a very genuine affection for her. He was full of gratitude for her devotion, and respect for her character; but there was always in his manner a nuance of superiority towards the woman who had given herself to him openly without marriage. Public opinion held that he could have contracted more honourable alliances. He did not say that to her, perhaps he did not say it to himself; but what is unsaid, exists nevertheless, and all that exists is guessed. Till then Ellenore had no notion of the passionate sentiment, the existence lost in her own, of which even my angers, my injustices and reproaches were only more certain proofs. Her resistance had keyed up all my sensations, all my ideas. I swung from transports which terrified her to submission, to tenderness, to idolatry. I looked upon her as a heavenly being. There was veneration in my love, and it charmed her the more because she was always fearful of being humiliated by others. At last she gave herself completely.

Woe to the man who, in the first moments of a love-liaison, does not believe that it must be eternal! Woe to the man who, in the arms of the mistress he has won, retains a deadly prescience and foresees that he will be able to part from them! A woman whom her heart leads to surrender, has in that moment something touching and sacred. It is not pleasure, not nature, not the senses which corrupt; but the calculations which society makes habitual, and the reflections born of experience. I loved, I revered Ellenore infinitely more after she had given herself. I walked with pride among men; I looked on them triumphantly. The air I breathed was in itself a delight. I rushed to Nature to thank her for the unhoped for and immeasurable blessing she had deigned to bestow on me.

# CHAPTER IV

The enchantment of love!  Who can depict it?  The conviction that we have found the being whom Nature destined for us, the sudden light which suffuses life and seems to explain its mystery, the preciousness attached to the tiniest circumstances, the swift hours whose details escape memory by their very sweetness and leave in our souls only a long scent of happiness, the playful gaiety which sometimes slips spontaneously into our habitual tenderness, the delight in presence and the hope in absence, the detachment from every sordid care, the superiority over all that surrounds us, the certainty that henceforward the world cannot reach the place where we truly live, the mutual attunement which divines every thought and responds to every emotion —the enchantment of love!  He who has not known it cannot describe it!

Count P——— had to go away for six weeks on urgent business.  I passed the time almost uninterruptedly with Ellenore.  Her attachment seemed increased by the sacrifice she had made.  She never let me leave her without trying to keep me.  When I went out, she asked when I would be back.  She could hardly bear two hours' separation.  She anxiously fixed the precise moment of my return.  I joyfully agreed.  I was grateful, I was happy at the feeling she showed for me.

Nevertheless, the interests of common life cannot be arbitrarily fitted to all our desires. It was sometimes inconvenient to me to have all my steps marked in advance and all my moments counted. I was compelled to hurry all my business, and break off most of my relations. I did not know what to reply to my acquaintances when they proposed a meeting which in a natural situation I should have had no reason to refuse. With Ellenore I did not in the least regret these pleasures of social life, which never attracted me particularly, but I would have preferred to renounce them more spontaneously. It would have been more delightful to go back to her of my own free will, without saying to myself: " It is time, she is anxiously waiting for me "; without the idea of her distress being mixed with the happiness of seeing her again. Ellenore was assuredly an acute pleasure in my existence, but she was no longer a goal: she had become a tie. And I was afraid of compromising her. My continual presence must surprise her servants and her children who could watch me. I trembled at the idea of upsetting her existence. I felt that we could not be united for ever, and that it was my sacred duty to respect her security. I gave her counsels of prudence, while assuring her of my love. But the more advice of this sort I gave her, the less was she inclined to listen. And I was dreadfully afraid of hurting her. As soon as I saw an expression of pain on her face, her will was mine: I was only at peace when she was pleased with me. When I insisted that I must go away for a little while and managed to leave her, the image of the pain I had caused her followed me everywhere. A fever of remorse seized me, which increased till it was irresistible: I flew back to her, anticipating the delight of consoling her. But as I approached her house a feeling of irritation against this queer tyranny was mixed with my other feelings.

Ellenore herself was tempestuous. I believe she felt for me what she had never felt for anyone. In her former relations, her heart was galled by her distressing dependence; with me, she was perfectly at ease, because we were perfectly equal; she had risen in her own eyes by a love which was pure of all calculation or interest; she knew that I was sure that she loved me only for myself. Because of her complete self-abandon with me she did not hide any of her feelings from me; and when I re-entered her room, sooner than I would and therefore impatient, I found her sad or annoyed. I had suffered for two hours away from her by the idea that she suffered away from me; I suffered two hours at her side before I could calm her.

But I was not unhappy; I said to myself that it was sweet to be loved, even though exactingly; I felt I was doing her good: her happiness was necessary to me, and I knew I was necessary to her happiness.

Besides, the dim idea that by the sheer nature of things this liaison could not last, saddening though it was in many ways, nevertheless served to quieten me in my fits of weariness or impatience. The bonds between Ellenore and Count P———, the disproportion of our ages, the difference of our situations, my departure (which had been delayed for many reasons, but now drew nearer)—all these considerations urged me to give and receive all the happiness I could. Certain of the years, I did not haggle over the days.

Count P——— returned. He quickly suspected my relations with Ellenore; every day his reception of me was colder and more morose. I spoke strongly to Ellenore of the dangers she ran; I begged her to let me interrupt my visits for a few days; to consider her reputation, her interests, her children. She listened to me in silence for a long while; she was deathly pale. "One way or another" (she said at last) "you will be going soon. Don't let us anticipate the moment. Don't worry about me. Let us gain days, gain hours. Days—hours—that is all I need. Adolphe, I have a presentiment that I shall die in your arms."

So we continued to live as before. I was always uneasy, Ellenore always sad, Count P——— silent and worried. At last came the letter I expected: my father ordered me home.

I took it to Ellenore. She read it, and said: "Already! I did not believe it would be so soon." Then, bursting into tears, she took my hand and said: "Adolphe, you see I cannot live without you; I do not know what will happen to my future, but I beseech you: do not go yet. Find excuses for staying. Ask your father for six months longer. Six months—is that so long?"

I tried to oppose her; but she wept so bitterly, she trembled so, there was such fearful suffering on her face, that I could not continue. I flung myself at her feet, I clasped her in my arms, I swore my love, and I went away to write to my father. I wrote with the emotion I felt at her pain. I produced a thousand reasons for delay; I emphasised the importance of my continuing at D—— various studies I had not been able to pursue at Göttingen. When I put my letter in the post, I ardently desired to obtain the consent I asked for.

That evening I returned to Ellenore. She was sitting on a sofa. Count P—— was near the fireplace, quite apart; the two children were at the end of the room; they were not playing, and on their faces was the consternation of children when they are aware of a tension, but do not know the cause. By a gesture I let Ellenore know I had done what she wanted. A gleam of joy shone in her eyes, then faded out. We said nothing. The silence was becoming embarrassing for all three of us. At last, " I am told, sir," said the Count to me, " that you are preparing to leave us." I replied that it was news to me. " I think that, at your age, one should lose no time in taking up a career; but," he added, looking at Ellenore, " perhaps not everybody here thinks as I do."

My father replied quickly. As I opened his letter I trembled at Ellenore's pain at a refusal. I even felt that the pain would be equally bitter to me; but as I read his consent, all the difficulties of a longer stay suddenly rose before my mind. " Six months' more misery and constraint!" I cried. " Six months' offending a man who has been friendly to me, six months' exposing a woman I love, six months' risk of robbing her of the only position in which she can live respected and at peace! I am deceiving my father. For what? To avoid for a moment facing the pain which sooner or later is inevitable. Don't we suffer this pain every day, by inches, drop by drop? I do nothing but harm to Ellenore. My feeling, as it now is, cannot satisfy her. I sacrifice myself for her, and she gains no happiness. I live here without profit without independence, without a moment of freedom, or an hour to breathe in peace."

Filled with these thoughts I went to Ellenore. She was alone. " I am staying another six months," I said.

" You tell me the news very coldly."

" Because I am deeply afraid, I confess, of
the consequences of this delay for both of us."

" I do not see how they can be very serious
for you, at least."

" You know perfectly well, Ellenore, that
I never think chiefly of myself."

" Nor of the happiness of others, either."

The conversation had taken a stormy turn.
Ellenore was hurt by my regrets at a moment
in which she felt I ought to share her joy;
I was hurt by her triumph over my previous
resolutions. The scene became violent. We
broke into mutual reproaches. Ellenore
accused me of deceiving her, of having had
only a passing fancy for her; of having
alienated the affection of the Count from her,
of having thrust her back, in the public eye,
into the equivocal position from which she had
tried all her life to escape. I was exasperated
because she turned against me what I had done
only in obedience, for her and for fear of
wounding her. I complained of my imprisoned
life, my youth wasted in inactivity, the tyranny
she exercised over all I tried to do. As I spoke,
I saw her face suddenly bathed in tears. I
stopped, I went back, I disavowed, I explained.
We kissed: but a first blow had been struck,
a first barrier crossed. Both had uttered
irreparable words; we could be silent, but we
could not forget them. There are things which
it takes long to say to oneself, but when once

they are said, one never stops repeating them.

We lived four months in this forced relation, sometimes sweet, never completely free, still finding pleasure in it, but no more enchantment. But Ellenore did not loose her hold on me. After our bitterest quarrels, she was just as eager to see me again, and fixed the time of our meetings just as carefully as though our union were full of peace and tenderness. I have often thought that my own behaviour helped to keep her in this disposition. If I had loved her as she loved me, she would have been calmer; she would herself have reflected on the dangers she defied. But all prudence was hateful to her, since the prudence came from me; she did not reckon her sacrifices, because she was bent on making me accept them; she had no time to grow colder towards me, because all her time and strength were taken in holding me. The new date fixed for my departure was drawing near. I thought of it with pleasure and regret: like a man who must pay for a certain cure by a painful operation.

One morning Ellenore wrote that I must go to her immediately. "The Count has forbidden me to receive you," she said. "I refuse to obey this tyranny. I followed him when he was banished, I saved his fortune; I have served his every interest. He can do without me now; but I cannot do without you."

It is easy to guess how I pressed her to

abandon a project which was unthinkable to me. I spoke of what the world would say. "The world has never been just to me," she said. "For ten years I have done my duty better than any woman; none the less the world has kept me from the position I deserved." I reminded her of her children. "My children are Count P———'s. He has acknowledged them. He will care for them. They will be happy to forget a mother who can leave them only shame." I implored her. "Listen!" she said. "If I break with the Count, will you refuse to see me? Will you refuse?" she repeated, seizing my arm with a violence that made me shudder.

"No—assuredly no," I replied. "And the unhappier you are, the more devoted I shall be. But think . . ."

"I have thought of everything," she interrupted. "He is coming back in a moment. Go away now; and do not come here again!"

I spent the rest of the day in indescribable distress. Two days passed without news of her. I suffered from not knowing what had happened to her; I suffered even from not seeing her, and I was astonished at the pain of this. Nevertheless I wanted her to abandon the resolve which I so greatly feared for her, and I was beginning to persuade myself she had, when a woman brought me a note from Ellenore begging me to go to see her in such and such a house and street, on the third floor.

I rushed there, still hoping that, since she could not receive me at the Count's house, she had made a rendezvous elsewhere for a last talk. I found her preparing a permanent establishment. She came to me, at once happy and shy, seeking to read my thoughts in my eyes.

"Everything is broken off," she said, "I am perfectly free. I have £75 a year of my own; it is enough for me. You are staying here another six weeks. When you leave, perhaps I can come near you; perhaps you will come back to see me." And, as though she would have dreaded a reply, she plunged into a mass of details about her plans. In every way she tried to persuade me that she would be happy, that she had sacrificed nothing for me, that what she had done was what she ought to have done—quite apart from me. It was plain that she was making a great effort over herself, and that she only half-believed what she was saying. She was bemusing herself with her own words, for fear of hearing mine: she busily spun out what she was saying to delay the moment when my objections would plunge her into despair again. I could not find it in my heart to make any. I accepted her sacrifice, and I thanked her for it, I said it made me happy; I said a great deal more: I assured her that I had always desired that an irreparable decision would make it my duty never to leave her; I attributed my waverings to a feeling of delicacy which forbade me to consent to anything that would ruin her situation. In a word, my only thought was to drive far away from her any hurt, any fear, any regret, any doubt as to my feeling for her. While I was speaking to her, that was my only aim, and I was sincere in my promises.

# CHAPTER V

The separation between Ellenore and the Count produced the expected effect upon opinion. In one instant she lost all she had gained by ten years' devotion and constancy; she was put with the women of her class who unhesitatingly plunge into a whole succession of affairs. Her leaving her children showed her an unnatural mother, and women of irreproachable reputation repeated unctuously that the neglect of the virtue most essential to their sex soon extends to all the others. At the same time they commiserated her, so as not to lose the pleasure of blaming me. My conduct was that of a seducer, an ingrate who had violated hospitality and, for the sake of a passing whim, sacrificed the peace of two persons—one to be respected, the other at least considered. Some friends of my father made serious representations to me; others, less forthright, made me feel their disapproval by indirect insinuations. The younger men, on the other hand, were delighted by the skill with which I had supplanted the Count; and in numerous pleasantries which I tried in vain to repress, they congratulated me on my conquest and said they would follow my example. I cannot describe what I suffered both from the stern censure and the shameful praise. I am convinced that if I had loved Ellenore I should have won opinion over to her and me. Such is the power of true feeling that, when it speaks, false interpretations and artificial conventions are dumb. But I was only a weak man, grateful and dominated; I was not sustained by any impulsion that came from the heart. So I expressed myself with embarrassment; I tried to put an end to the conversation; and if it continued, I ended it with a few rough words which told the others that I was ready to pick a quarrel. And indeed I would sooner have fought them than replied.

Ellenore was quickly aware that opinion had risen against her. Two relatives of Count P———— whom his influence had forced to recognise her, broke with her demonstratively, delighted to give reign to their malice, which had so long been repressed, behind the austere principles of morality. The men continued to see Ellenore; but now in their tone was a tinge of familiarity which indicated that she was no longer upheld by a powerful protector, nor justified by a union almost consecrated. Some visited her because (they said) they had always known her; others because she was still beautiful, and her recent behaviour had reawakened pretentions which they did not try to disguise from her. All gave reasons for their connection with her; which meant that all felt that the connection needed explanation. So the unfortunate Ellenore saw herself fallen for ever into the condition from which all her life she had tried to emerge. Everything combined to bruise her soul and wound her pride. She looked on her abandonment by some as a proof of contempt, and the assiduity of the others as the sign of some insulting expectation. Solitude made her suffer, society made her blush.

Ah, no doubt, I should have consoled her; I should have clasped her against my heart, and said: "Let us live for each other; let us forget those who cannot understand us; let us find all our happiness in our own esteem and love." I tried to do thus; but what power has a resolve taken by duty to rekindle a dying sentiment?

Ellenore and I pretended with one another. She dared not tell me of her sufferings from a sacrifice which she knew I had not asked from her. I had accepted the sacrifice. I dared not complain of a misfortune I had foreseen, but was not strong enough to avert. So we said nothing of the one thought which was always in our minds. We were prodigal of caresses, we talked of love; but we talked of love for fear we might talk of something else.

As soon as there is a secret between two loving hearts, as soon as one is resolved to hide from the other a single thought, the charm is broken, the happiness destroyed. Anger, injustice, even neglect, can be repaired; but dissimulation brings into love an alien element which denatures and blights it in its own eyes.

By a queer inconsequence, while I repelled

with the utmost indignation the slightest in-
sinuation against Ellenore, I myself helped to
wrong her in my general conversation. I had
submitted to her wishes, but I had conceived
a horror of the regiment of women. I de-
claimed incessantly against their weakness,
their exigence, the tyranny of their grief. I
proclaimed the sternest principles; and the
same man who could not resist a tear, who suc-
cumbed to a look of sadness, who was haunted
in absence by the image of the suffering he
had caused, showed himself contemptuous and
merciless in all his speeches. Nor could all
my direct praise of Ellenore destroy the impression made by this kind of talk. They
hated me, they commiserated her; but they did
not esteem her. They held it against her that
she had not inspired her lover with more consideration for her sex and more respect for
the bond of love.

After her rupture with Count P——, a
man who habitually visited Ellenore fell
violently in love with her and by his indiscreet
insistences forced her to refuse to receive him:
he then indulged in outrageous jests about her
which I found intolerable. We fought a duel;
I wounded him dangerously and was wounded
myself. I cannot describe the confusion of
alarm, of terror, of gratitude and of love, on
Ellenore's face when she saw me afterwards.
Although I besought her not to, she stayed in
my rooms and did not leave me for a moment

until I was convalescent. She read to me in the daytime; and watched over me most of the night. She observed my least movement, and anticipated every desire; her ingenious kindness gave her new faculties and doubled her strength. She assured me incessantly that she would not have survived me. I was pierced with affection, and torn by remorse. If only I could have found in myself something to recompense so constant and tender an attachment! I called to my aid memories, imagination, reason even, the feeling of duty—all in vain! The difficulty of the situation, the certainty that the future would separate us, perhaps a kind of revolt against a bond which I could not break, devoured me within. I reproached myself for the ingratitude which I tried to conceal from her. I was tormented when she seemed to doubt a love which was so necessary to her; I was equally tormented when she seemed to believe in it. I felt she was nobler than I, and I despised myself for being unworthy of her. It is a terrible thing not be loved when one loves; but it is far more terrible to be loved passionately when one loves no longer. I had just risked my life for Ellenore, I would have given it up over and over again for her to be happy without me.

The six months my father had allowed me were now gone; I had to think of my departure. Ellenore did not oppose it, she did not even try to delay it; but she made me promise that

I would either return to her after two months, or let her rejoin me. I solemnly swore it. What would I not have promised at a moment when I saw her struggling with herself to restrain her grief? She could have made me stay with her: deep in my soul I knew I could not have disobeyed her tears. I was grateful that she did not exert her power over me; I felt I loved her the more for it. And I had pangs of regret at parting from a being so utterly devoted to me. There is something so profound in a long liaison. Unconsciously it becomes such an intimate part of our existence. At a distance we calmly form the resolve to break it; we believe we are waiting impatiently to carry it out: but when the moment arrives, it fills us with terror, and such is the contrariness of our wretched heart that it is a horrible laceration to leave those with whom it was no pleasure to stay.

While I was away, I wrote regularly to Ellenore. I was torn between the fear that my letters would give her pain, and the longing to tell only the truth about what I felt. I wanted her to read me between the lines, but to do it without suffering; I congratulated myself when I managed to substitute the words "affection," "friendship," "devotion" for "love"; but suddenly I pictured poor Ellenore sad and alone, with only my letters to console her, and at the end of two cold and formal pages, I quickly added some passionate or tender phrases calculated to deceive her once more. So, while never saying enough to satisfy her, I always said enough to impose upon her. Strange deception! Its success turned against me, prolonged my anguish, and was unbearable.

Anxiously I counted the days, the hours; I longed to slow the march of time; I trembled as the time to fulfil my promise drew near. I could imagine no means of leaving; I could discover no means of Ellenore's coming to live in the same city. Perhaps—to be sincere—I did not desire it. I compared my tranquil and independent life with the life of hurry, trouble and torment to which her passion condemned me. I found it so good to be free, to come and go, to depart and return, with nobody to care. It was as though in the indifference of others I found rest from the strain of her love.

But I dared not let Ellenore suspect that I would have liked to abandon our plans. She understood from my letters that it would be difficult for me to leave my father; and she wrote to me that, in consequence, she was herself preparing to leave. For a long while I did not oppose her resolve; I answered vaguely on the subject. Then I hinted that I should always be enchanted to know that she was happy—I added, to *make* her happy. Miserable equivocations, embarrassed words, that I groaned to see so obscure, and was frightened to make clearer! Finally, I made up my mind to speak frankly to her; I told myself it was my duty; I roused my conscience against my weakness; I fortified myself with the idea of her peace against the image of her grief. I strode up and down the room, reciting aloud what I proposed to say to her. I had hardly written a line when my disposition changed. I no longer saw in my words what they ought to convey, but the effect they could not fail to produce. A supernatural power controlled my hand in spite of myself, and I did no more than advise a few months' delay. I had not said what I thought. My letter had no stamp of sincerity. The reasons I produced were feeble, because they were not the true ones.

Ellenore's reply was impetuous; she was indignant at my desire not to see her. What did she ask of me? Only to live near me, unknown. What could I dread from her presence in a secret hiding-place, in a great city where no one was acquainted with her? She has sacrificed everything to me—fortune, children, reputation; the only return she asked was to attend me like a humble slave, to spend with me a few minutes of every day, to enjoy the moments I could spare her. She had resigned herself to two months' absence, not because it seemed to her necessary, but because I seemed to desire it; and now when by painfully adding day to day, she had come to the date I myself had fixed, I proposed that she should begin the long torment again! Perhaps she had made a mistake, perhaps she had given her life to a hard unfeeling man. I was master of my actions, but I could not force her to suffer, abandoned by the man for whom she had made a holocaust of everything.

Ellenore quickly followed her letter. She let me know of her arrival. I went to her firmly resolved to show great joy; I was impatient to reassure her heart and bring her happiness or calm, at least for the moment. But she had been wounded; she examined me mistrustfully; she soon detected my efforts; she stung my pride by her reproaches; she insulted my character. She made my weakness appear so pitiable that I was angrier with her than with myself. A mad fury seized us: we flung aside all reserve, forgot all delicacy. We were hounded against each other by Furies. All that implacable hatred had invented against us both, we applied to one another; and these two unhappy beings, known by each other alone upon this earth, who alone could do each other justice, understand and comfort each other, were like two mortal enemies, ravening to destroy each other.

It lasted three hours before we parted; for the first time in our life we left each other without explanation or amends. I had hardly left Ellenore when my anger gave way to an access of grief. I was in a kind of stupor, stunned by what had passed. I repeated my words, and they astounded me; I found my own behaviour unthinkable; I searched in myself to find what could have crazed me so.

It was very late: I dared not return to Ellenore. I vowed to see her early the next morning, and I returned to my father's house. There were many guests; it was easy in such a crowd to keep out of the way and hide my distress. When we were alone, my father said: " I am told that the former mistress of Count P——— is in this city. I have always allowed you great liberty, and I have never desired to know anything about your liaisons; but at your age it is not proper to have an avowed mistress; and I warn you that I have taken measures to send her away from here." Having said this, he left me.

I followed him to his room. He signed to me to go away. "Father," I said, "God is my witness that I want her to be happy, and that for this I would consent never to see her again. But take care what you do. You think you are separating us; you may be attaching me to her for ever."

Immediately I summoned a manservant who had accompanied me on my travels and knew of my relations with Ellenore. I ordered him to find out immediately, if he could, the measures of which my father had spoken. In two hours he returned. My father's secretary had told him, under the seal of secrecy, that Ellenore was to be served with an order of expulsion the next day. "Ellenore driven out!" I cried. "Driven out in ignominy! Who came here only for me, whose heart I have broken, whose tears I have watched without pity! Where shall she rest her head—unfortunate, wandering alone in a world of whose esteem I have robbed her? To whom can she confide her pain?"

My decision was soon taken. I won over my servant with money and promises. I ordered a post-chaise to be at the city-gate at six in the morning. I formed endless projects for my everlasting reunion with Ellenore; I loved her more than I had ever loved her; my whole heart had returned to her; I was proud to protect her. I was hungry to hold her in my arms; love entire had repossessed my soul; there was a fever in my head, my heart, my senses, which convulsed my existence. If at that moment Ellenore had wanted to part from me, I would have died at her feet to hold her back.

Day broke; I rushed to Ellenore. She was still in bed, for she had spent the night weeping; her eyes were still wet, her hair dishevelled. She was surprised to see me. "Come," I said, "let us go away!" She tried to answer. "Let us go away! Have you any protector, any friend on earth except me? My arms are your only refuge." She still resisted. "I have important reasons," I added, "reasons of my own. In heaven's name, follow me!"

65

I swept her away. During the journey I smothered her with caresses, I pressed her to my heart, I answered all her questions with kisses. At last I told her that when I saw that my father intended to separate us, I had felt that I could not be happy without her; that I wanted to devote my life to her, and bind her to me with every possible bond. At first, she was all gratitude; but she soon found contradictions in my story. By her insistence she got the truth out of me. Her joy vanished, and a cloud came over her face.

"Adolphe," she said, "you mistake yourself. You are generous; you devote yourself to me because I am persecuted; you think it is love, but it is only pity."

Why did she speak these fatal words? Why did she reveal to me a secret I wanted to ignore? I strove to reassure her, and perhaps I succeeded; but the truth had passed through my soul: the emotion was destroyed. I was resolved in my sacrifice, but it no longer made me happy; and already there was in my mind a thought which I was again compelled to hide.

# CHAPTER VI

When we reached the frontier, I wrote to my father. My letter was respectful, but there was bitterness beneath. I took it hard that he had tightened my bonds, intending to break them. I told him that I should not leave Ellenore until she was decently settled and had no more need of me. I begged him not to force me to be attached to her for ever, by being vindictive against her. I waited for his reply before taking a decision about our establishment. "You are twenty-four," he replied. "I shall not bring to bear on you an authority which is almost at an end, and which I have never used. I shall even hush up your strange doings as far as I can; I shall spread the report that you have left at my orders, on business for me. I will give you a generous allowance. You yourself will soon come to feel that the life you are leading is not worthy of you. Your birth, your talents, your fortune give you another place in society than that of the companion of a woman without a country or a home. As it is, your letter proves to me that you are not pleased with yourself. Remember you gain nothing by prolonging a situation of which you are ashamed. You are wasting the best years of your youth, and that loss is irreparable."

My father's letter stabbed me through and through. How often I had said to myself what he said to me, and been ashamed that my life was dribbling away in obscurity and inaction! I would sooner he had reproached and threatened me; I would have found some glory in resisting him; I should have felt the necessity of gathering my strength together to protect Ellenore from the perils which would have assailed her. But there were no perils; I was left perfectly free; and my freedom served only to make me more impatient of the yoke I seemed to have chosen myself.

We settled at Caden, a little town in Bohemia. I repeated to myself that since I had taken the responsibility for Ellenore's fate, I must not make her suffer. I managed to restrain myself; I kept the smallest signs of discontent tight shut in my heart, and I employed all the resources of my mind to create an artificial gaiety to conceal my sadness. This effort had an unexpected effect upon me. We are such changeable creatures that we end by feeling the feelings we feign. I partly forgot the griefs I hid. My flow of lively talk dispelled my own melancholy. My tender assurances to Ellenore spread a sweet emotion in my soul which was very like love.

From time to time importunate memories beset me. When I was alone, I was a prey to fits of uneasiness; I formed countless queer plans for suddenly breaking out of the existence in which I was falsely placed. But I suppressed these emotions as bad dreams.

Ellenore seemed happy; could I trouble her happiness? Nearly five months passed in this fashion.

One day I saw that Ellenore was agitated, and trying to keep from me a thought which preoccupied her. I pressed her hard, and at last she made me promise that I would not oppose the decision she had taken, and confessed that Count P——— had written to her. He had won his law-suit, and he gratefully recalled the services she had done him, and their ten years' connection. He offered her half his fortune, not to return to him—that was now impossible—but on condition she left the treacherous ingrate who had separated them. " I have replied," she said, " and you can guess that I have refused." I had guessed only too well. I was touched; but Ellenore's fresh sacrifice drove me to despair. But I dared not object; all my efforts of that kind had been so fruitless. I went apart to reflect on what I ought to do. It was clear that our relations ought to be broken off. They were painful to me; they were becoming positively harmful to her: I was the only obstacle to her regaining a decent position and the respect which in society sooner or later attends on wealth; I was the only barrier between her and her children; I was now without excuse in my own eyes. To give way to her in these circumstances was no longer generosity, but culpable weakness. I had promised my father to regain my freedom as soon as I was no longer necessary to Ellenore. And it was time to enter a career, to begin an active life, to acquire a few claims to men's esteem, and make an honourable use of my capacities. I went back to Ellenore, with the unshakable resolve (as I believed) to force her to accept the offer of Count P———, and if it were necessary, to declare that I was no longer in love with her.

"My dear," I said, "one struggles for a time against one's destiny; but one ends by yielding to it. The laws of society are stronger than the wills of men; the most imperious feelings break themselves against the fatality of circumstances. We insist on listening only to our hearts—in vain: we are condemned to listen to reason at last. I cannot keep you any longer in a position equally unworthy of us both."

As I went on speaking without looking at Ellenore, I felt my ideas becoming vaguer, and my resolution weaken. To pull myself together, I went on hurriedly:

"I shall always be your friend; I shall always have the deepest affection for you. The two years we have been together will be in-effaceable in my memory; they will always be the loveliest period of my life. But love—that transport of the senses, that involuntary in-toxication, that oblivion of every interest and every duty—I have it no longer, Ellenore."

I waited an age for her reply, without

ʌaising my eyes to her. When at last I **did**
look at her, she was quite still; she looked **at**
everything as though she could not have recognised it: I took her hand, it was cold. She
drew away. "What do you want?" she said.
"Am I not alone in the universe, alone—
without a soul to understand? What more
have you to say to me? Have you not said
everything? Is not everything finished—
finished irrevocably? Go away, leave me! Is
that not what you desire?"

She tried to move away, but she tottered;
I tried to hold her back, she fell unconscious
at my feet. I lifted her up, I kissed her, I
brought her to her senses.

"Ellenore!" I cried. "Come back to
yourself! Come back to me! I love you—
truly and tenderly. I told you false, to make
you freer in your choice!"

The credulity of the heart is inexplicable!
These simple words, belied by so many before,
restored Ellenore to life and confidence. She
made me repeat them several times, she seemed
eager to breathe. She believed me; she was
intoxicated by her own love, which she took
for ours. She confirmed her reply to the Count,
and I was more deeply committed than ever.

Three months later, there was a new possibility of change in Ellenore's situation. One
of those turns of fortune common in faction-
ridden countries brought her father back to
Poland and restored him to his property.

Although he hardly knew his daughter, whom her mother had taken to France at three years old, he wanted to settle her at his side. Only the vaguest report of Ellenore's adventures had reached him in Russia, where he had lived continually during his exile. Ellenore was his only child. He was afraid of being lonely; he wanted to be looked after; his one object was to find where she was living, and as soon as he had discovered it, he pressed her to return to him. She could have no real attachment to a father whom she could not remember having seen. Nevertheless, she felt it her duty to obey; for so she would secure a great fortune to her children, and herself return to the rank of which her misfortunes and her conduct had deprived her. But she said outright that she would not return to Poland unless I went with her.

"I am at an age," she said, "when the soul is no longer open to new impressions. My father is a stranger to me. If I stay here, others will eagerly gather round him, and he will be just as happy. My children will inherit their father's fortune. I know well that everybody will blame me for an ungrateful daughter and an unfeeling mother; but I have suffered too much; I am no longer young enough to be greatly affected by what the world thinks. If there is something hard in my resolve, Adolphe, you must blame yourself. If I could have any illusion about you, I might consent to our parting; because its bitterness would be diminished by the prospect of a sweet and lasting reunion. But you would ask nothing better than to believe I was six hundred miles away from you, happy and at peace, in the midst of my family and surrounded by wealth. Then you could write me such reasonable letters; I can see them now; they would tear my heart to pieces. I do not want to expose myself to that. I have not the consolation of telling myself that by the sacrifice of my whole life I have inspired in you the sentiment I deserved; but you did accept the sacrifice. I suffer enough already from the constraint of your attitude and the coldness of our relations. I can submit to the sufferings you inflict upon me; but I will not inflict them upon myself."

There was a kind of roughness and violence in Ellenore's voice and tone which indicated a firm determination rather than a deep or touching emotion. For some time past she had been irritated beforehand when she asked anything of me, as though I had already refused it. She was mistress of my actions, but she knew that my judgment disowned them. She would have liked to penetrate into the secret places of my thought to break the silent opposition which roused her anger against me. I spoke of my situation, my father's wishes, my own desire; I pleaded, I lost my temper. Ellenore was immovable. I tried to awaken her generosity, as though love were not the most selfish of all feelings and in consequence, when it is wounded, the least generous. I made a fantastic effort to soften her heart towards my unhappiness in staying with her: I merely exasperated her. I promised to go and see her in Poland; but my promises did not come from an eager and overflowing heart, and she saw in them only my impatience to leave her.

We had lived a year at Caden, and nothing had changed in our situation. When Ellenore found me gloomy and depressed, she would be sad at first, then wounded, and finally her reproaches would sting me to confess the weariness I wanted to hide from her. When she seemed content, I was irritated to see her happy in a situation which cost me my happiness, and I spoiled her short-lived joy by my intimations of what I really felt. Then we attacked each other in turn in veiled phrases, then retreated into abstract protestations and vague self-justifications, and finally relapsed into silence. We knew so well everything that we were going to say to each other, that we kept quiet to avoid hearing it. Sometimes one of us was ready to yield, but we missed the moment to come together. Our suspicious and wounded hearts no longer met.

I often asked myself why I remained in this pitiful situation. I replied that, if I left Ellenore, she would follow me, and I should provoke yet another sacrifice. Finally I said to myself that I must give her this last satisfaction, and that she could demand nothing more of me when I had replaced her in the midst of her family. I was on the point of offering to go with her to Poland, when she received the news that her father was dead. He had made her his sole heir, but his will was contradicted by subsequent letters to which her distant relatives threatened to appeal. In spite of her little contact with her father, Ellenore was painfully affected by his death. She reproached herself for having abandoned him. Soon she blamed me for it. " You made me fail in a sacred duty," she said. " Now, only my own fortune is concerned. I will sacrifice it for you even more readily. But I will certainly not go alone into a country where I have only enemies to meet." " I never wanted you to fail in any duty," I said. " I confess, I would have liked you to condescend to reflect that it hurt me, too, to fail in mine. I could not obtain this justice from you, I surrender, Ellenore. Your interest triumphs over every other consideration. We will set off together when you like."

And so we did. The distractions of the journey, the novelty of the scenes, the restraint we imposed upon ourselves, occasionally rekindled the ashes of our intimacy. We were so accustomed to each other, we had lived through so many vicissitudes together, that every word, every gesture almost, awakened memories which suddenly put us back in the past, and filled us with tenderness despite ourselves, as lightning breaks through the darkness, but does not dispel it. We lived, as it were, on a kind of memory of the heart, powerful enough to make the idea of separation painful, but too weak to make us find happiness in being united. I found rest from my habitual constraint by surrendering myself to these emotions. I would have liked to give Ellenore evidences of tenderness which would have made her happy; I sometimes spoke the language of love; but the emotions and the language were like the pale and discoloured leaves which, by a lingering impulse of life, grow languidly on the branches of an uprooted tree.

# CHAPTER VII

On her arrival, Ellenore was allowed to take possession of the disputed property on condition she did not dispose of it until the case was decided. She established herself on one of her father's estates. My father, who never discussed anything directly in his letters to me, contented himself with filling them with insinuations against my journey. "You informed me," he wrote, "that you would not go. You expounded at length all the reasons you had for not going. Consequently, I was quite convinced that you would go. I can only commiserate you because, with your independent spirit, you always do what you do not want to do. For the rest I pass no judgment on a situation with which I am imperfectly acquainted. Up till now you appeared to be Ellenore's protector. From that aspect there was a certain nobility in your doings which raised your character, whatever the object of its attachment. Now your relations are changed: you no longer protect her; she protects you. You live at her house; you are a stranger she has introduced into her family. I do not pronounce on a situation which you have chosen; but since it may have its disadvantages, I should like to mitigate them as far as I can. I am writing to Baron T———, our Minister in the country in which you are, to recommend you to him. I do not know

77

whether it will suit you to make use of this recommendation. But look upon it at least as a proof of my devotion, and not at all as an attempt to diminish the independence which you have always defended successfully against your father."

I suppressed the reflections which this manner of writing inspired in me. The estate where I was living with Ellenore was quite near Warsaw. I went to see Baron T——— in the city. He gave me a friendly reception, asked the reasons for my stay in Poland, and questioned me on my plans: I was embarrassed to reply. After a few minutes' conversation, he said to me:

"I am going to speak frankly. I know why you have come to this country. Your father has informed me. I may even say that I understand your motives. There is not a man who has not known, once in his life, what it is to be torn between the desire to break an unsuitable liaison and the fear of hurting the woman he has loved. The inexperience of youth vastly exaggerates the difficulties of such a situation; it is inclined to believe in the truth of all those demonstrations of suffering which take the place of the weapons of strength and reason in the weaker and more excitable sex. One's heart may suffer, but one's self-esteem is gratified; and the man who, in all good faith, believes he is sacrificing himself to the despair he has caused, is in fact sacri-

ficing himself only to the illusions of his own
vanity. The world is full of passionate women :
every one of them has cried that she would
die if she were abandoned; every one of them
is still alive and has found consolation." I
wanted to interrupt him. " Forgive me, my
young friend, if I speak rather brutally; but
the good report I have of you, your evident
talents, the career you ought to be following
—all these compel me to speak frankly. I can
read your soul, in spite of you and better than
you. You are no longer in love with the woman
who dominates you and drags you after her.
If you still loved her, you would not have come
to me. You knew your father had written to
me; it was easy for you to guess what I had
to say to you; you were not angry at hearing
from me arguments which you are continually
repeating to yourself, but always in vain.
Ellenore's reputation is far from intact."

" Pray, let us not continue this useless
conversation," I replied. " Unhappy circumstances determined Ellenore's early life. She
can be judged harshly on deceitful appearances :
but I have known her three years, and there
does not exist on the earth a loftier soul, a
nobler character, a purer and more generous
heart."

" As you please," he replied, " but these
are nuances into which public opinion does not
enter. The facts are positive and public. Do
you think you can abolish them by preventing

me from speaking of them? Listen," he went on, " in this world one must know what one wants. Will you marry Ellenore?"

" No, I suppose not," I cried. " She herself has never wanted that."

" Then what do you mean to do? She is ten years older than you. You are twenty-six. You will look after her for another ten years. She will be old, and you will have reached middle-age without having begun, much less completed, anything which satisfies you. You will be bored, she will be irritated. Every day she will be less delightful to you, you more necessary to her. And the end of good birth, a fine fortune and a distinguished mind will be to vegetate in a corner of Poland, forgotten by your friends, lost to fame, and tormented by a woman who will never be content with you whatever you do. I will only add this— and then we will not return to a subject which embarrasses you. All roads are open to you— literature, the army, the civil service; you may aspire to the most distinguished marriages, you have the gifts to achieve anything: but remember this: between you and every kind of success there is one insurmountable obstacle —and that obstacle is Ellenore."

" I thought it my duty, sir," I replied, " to listen to you in silence; but I owe it to myself to make plain that you have not shaken me. I repeat, only I can judge Ellenore; nobody else appreciates the truth of her senti-

ments and the depth of her feelings. As long
as she needs me, I shall stay with her. No
kind of success could ever console me for
having left her unhappy; and if my career were
to be confined to giving her something to lean
on, to supporting her in her sufferings, to protecting her by my affection from the injustice
of a world which misunderstands her, I should
still believe my life had not been wasted."

With these words I left him. But how
explain the fickleness by which the sentiment
which inspired the words faded even before I
had finished speaking them? I walked home,
in order to postpone seeing Ellenore, though I
had just been defending her. I hurried through
the city; I was in haste to be alone.

When I had reached the country, I
slowed my pace, and a crowd of thoughts
assailed me. The fatal words echoed round
me: "Between you and every kind of success
there is one insurmountable obstacle, and that
obstacle is Ellenore." I looked long and sadly
at the time now irrevocably past; I recalled
the hopes of my youth, the confident command
of the future I used to feel, the praise my first
attempts had won, the dawning reputation
which I had seen glow and disappear. I
repeated the names of several of my fellow-
students, for whom I had felt a lofty disdain,
yet who, simply by stubborn application and
a life of routine, had left me far behind on the
road to fortune, consideration and fame. I

was oppressed by my inactivity. As a miser
sees in the wealth he accumulates all the good
things that the wealth might buy, I saw in
Ellenore the deprivation of all the successes to
which I could have aspired. It was not only
one career that I regretted; having attempted
none, I regretted them all. Having never
made trial of my powers, I imagined them unlimited, and cursed them. I wished nature
had made me feeble and mediocre, to save me
at least from the remorse of having degraded
myself. Praise or approval of my intelligence
or my knowledge seemed an intolerable reproach: like admiration of the muscles of an
athlete loaded with chains in a dungeon. If
I tried to pluck up my courage and tell myself
that the time for activity was not yet past, the
image of Ellenore rose before me like a ghost
and thrust me back into nothingness. I had
fits of rage against her, yet, by a queer contradiction this rage did not lessen the terror I
felt at the idea of hurting her.

Wearied by these bitter feelings my mind
sought refuge in their contraries. Baron
T———'s casual words about the possibility
of a mild and peaceful marriage induced the
vision of an ideal mate. I thought of the tranquillity, the consideration, the independence I
should gain from such a prize: for the bonds
I had trailed so long made me infinitely more
dependent than a recognised union would have
done. I pictured my father's joy; I had an im-

patient desire to recapture the place in my own country and the society of my equals which was my due; I imagined my decorous and irreproachable conduct controverting all the judgments which cold and frivolous malignity had pronounced against me, and all the reproaches heaped on me by Ellenore.

"She accuses me incessantly," I said to myself, "of being hard, ungrateful and pitiless. If only heaven had granted me a woman whom convention allowed me to acknowlege, whom my father would not blush to accept as his daughter, how much happier I should have been to make her happy. My tenderness is misunderstood because it is wounded and suffers; it is imperiously summoned to produce evidences of itself, and my heart refuses them to passion and threats. How sweet it would be to surrender to it with the beloved being, the companion of a regular and respected life! What have I not done for Ellenore? For her I have abandoned my country and my family; for her I have pained the heart of an old father who grieves far away; for her I live in this place where my youth slips by in solitude, without fame, without honour, without pleasure. I have made all these sacrifices without the call of duty or love—do they not prove what I could do at their call? If I am so terrified of the suffering of a woman who dominates me only by her suffering, how devotedly would I shield from every hurt and pain the

woman to whom I could dedicate myself
without remorse or reserve? How different I
should appear from what I now am! How
quickly and completely would disappear the
bitterness for which men condemn me because
they do not know its cause! How grateful to
God I should be—and how kindly to men!"

While I spoke my eyes filled with tears,
torrents of memories poured into my soul—
memories which my relation with Ellenore
had made hateful. Everything which recalled
my childhood—the places where my first years
were spent, my early playmates, the elderly
relatives who were the first to show signs of
interest in me—hurt me and made me wince.
I was reduced to repelling the sweetest memories and the most natural longings as though
they were criminal thoughts. But the companion whom my fancy had suddenly created
was in harmony with all these memories, and
made all these longings legitimate; she shared
all my duties, my pleasures and my tastes;
she joined my present life to the period of my
youth when hope displayed a boundless future
before me—a period from which Ellenore had
separated me by an abyss. My memory re-
traced the tiniest details: I saw the old château
where I lived with my father, the surrounding
woods, the river which flowed beneath its
walls, the mountains on the horizon. All these
became so vivid, so full of life, that I could
hardly bear my agitation. And my fantasy

set beside them a young and innocent girl who made them more beautiful and alive with hope. Plunged in this dream I wandered on, without any fixed plan, never saying to myself that I must break with Ellenore, having only a dull confused idea of reality, like a grief-stricken man who has been consoled by a dream, but who feels that the end of the dream is near. Suddenly I saw Ellenore's château before me, which I had approached unawares. I stopped and took another road, glad to delay the moment when I should hear her voice again.

The day was dying; the sky was clear; the fields were deserted; the labours of men had ceased, leaving nature to herself. Gradually my thoughts took a graver and more impressive tinge. Every moment the shades of night grew thicker; the vast silence which surrounded me was broken only by infrequent sounds from far away; it replaced my fantasy by a calmer and more solemn feeling. I looked round the grey horizon. Its limits were now invisible, and it gave me the sensation of immensity. It was long since I had experienced anything like this. Everlastingly absorbed in personal reflections, my eyes always fixed on my own situation, I had become a stranger to impersonal ideas. I was occupied only with Ellenore and myself—with Ellenore who inspired only pity and weariness in me, with myself whom I now despised. I had shrunk into a new kind of egotism—

egotism without courage, malcontent and humiliated. I was thankful to become alive to thoughts of a different order, to find myself once more capable of forgetting myself and surrendering to disinterested meditations. My soul seemed to rouse up from a long and shameful degradation.

Nearly the whole night passed thus. I walked at random; I passed through fields, woods, villages, where everything was still. From time to time I caught from some distant dwelling a pale gleam which pierced the darkness. "There perhaps," I said, "some unfortunate tosses in pain, or struggles against death—the inexplicable mystery of which men's daily experience seems not even yet to have convinced them: the certain end which neither consoles us nor calms us, towards which men feel an habitual carelessness and a fleeting fear. And I, too, yield to this mad inconsequence! I revolt against life as though life would never end. I spread unhappiness round me, to recapture a few wretched years which time will soon snatch from me! Ah, give up these futile efforts; rejoice to see the time pass, the days rushing one after another; remain unmoved, the indifferent spectator of an existence half spent! Seize hold of it, tear it to shreds: you will not make it longer. Is it worth struggling over?"

The idea of death has always had great power over me. When my emotions have been most deeply disturbed, it has always sufficed to calm me immediately. It produced its accustomed effect on me; I became less bitter towards Ellenore. All my irritation vanished; from my night of delirium only a mild and almost tranquil sentiment remained. Perhaps it was partly due to my physical weariness.

Day was breaking; I could distinguish objects now. I saw that I was far away from Ellenore's house. I pictured to myself her anxiety, and I was hurrying to get back to her, as fast as my weariness allowed, when I met a mounted servant she had sent to look for me. He told me she had been terribly alarmed for twelve hours. She had gone to Warsaw; she had searched the outskirts, and had returned home in indescribable anguish. The villagers had been sent out in all directions to find me. At first, the story irritated me painfully. I was annoyed at Ellenore's irksome surveillance. It was no good telling myself that her love was the only cause. Was it not also the cause of all my unhappiness? However, I was ashamed of the feeling and conquered it. I knew she was alarmed and suffering. I mounted and rode quickly home. She received me with transports of joy. I was moved by her emotion. We talked but little, for she soon had the idea that I must be needing rest. I left her, this time at least without having said anything to wound her heart.

# CHAPTER VIII

When I rose the next day I was beset by
the same ideas which had disturbed me the
day before. On the following days my agitation increased. Ellenore tried to discover the
cause, in vain; I replied to her impetuous questions in constrained monosyllables; I stiffened
myself against her insistence, knowing only
too well that the consequence of my frankness
would be her pain, and that her pain would
compel me to fresh dissimulation.

Surprised and uneasy, she went to a
woman friend to discover the secret she
accused me of hiding from her. She was
eager to deceive herself, and looked for a fact
where there was only a feeling. Her friend
talked to me about my queer moods, my
sedulous rejection of the idea of a lasting connection, my inexplicable longing for rupture
and isolation. I listened to her in silence for
a long while. Until then I had never told anybody that I was no longer in love with
Ellenore; my lips refused to confess it,
because it seemed a perfidy. But I wanted to
justify myself. I told my story with restraint,
I heaped praise on Ellenore, I admitted the in-
consistencies of my behaviour, and blamed
them on the difficulties of our situation, and I
did not utter a word to show clearly that the
true difficulty was the absence of love in me.
Her friend was moved by my story: she saw

generosity in what I called weakness, unhappiness in what I called harshness. The same explanations which roused the passionate Ellenore to fury brought conviction to the mind of her impartial friend. Never trust another with the interests of your heart! The heart alone can plead its own cause, and probe its wounds. The intermediary always becomes a judge; analyses, compromises, entertains the idea of indifference, admits it as possible, recognises it as inevitable; thereby excuses it. And indifference, to its own astonishment, becomes legitimate in its own eyes. Ellenore's reproaches had convinced me that I had done wrong; I learnt from her defender that I was only unhappy. I was drawn on to make a clean breast of my feelings. I avowed that I felt devotion, sympathy, pity for Ellenore; but I added that love had nothing to do with the duties I imposed upon myself. This truth I had kept close in my heart, and revealed to Ellenore only in the heat of agitation and anger, now gained force and reality by the mere fact that I had confided it to someone else. It is a crucial step, an irrevocable step, when one suddenly reveals to the eyes of a third person the hidden places of an intimate relation. The light of day which penetrates the sanctuary reveals and completes the destruction which was covered by the shadow of night. Bodies in tombs often keep their shape, until the outside air strikes them and reduces them to dust.

Ellenore's friend went away. I do not
know what account she gave her of our conversation; but as I came towards the salon
I heard Ellenore's excited voice. When she
saw me, she stopped. Soon she began some
general statements which, in various forms,
were particular attacks. "There is nothing
more peculiar," she said, "than the zeal of
some friends. There are people who are eager
to take charge of your interests, only to abandon your cause more completely. They call
it attachment; I prefer hatred." I easily understood that Ellenore's friend had taken my
part against her, and had irritated her by not
judging me sufficiently in the wrong. I felt
myself almost in league with another against
Ellenore: it was one more barrier between our
hearts.

A few days later, Ellenore went further.
She was incapable of controlling herself.
When she thought she had cause of offence,
she went straight for an explanation, without
consideration or calculation. She preferred
the risk of a breach to the constraint of pretence. The two friends parted, embroiled for
ever.

"Why bring strangers into our intimate
discussions?" I said to Ellenore. "Do we
need a third to make us agree? And if we
agree no longer, what third person can help
us?"

" You are right," she said. " But it is your fault. I used not to need to go to anybody else to reach your heart."

Suddenly, Ellenore announced that she was going to change her way of life. I gathered from what she said that she blamed the solitude in which we lived for the discontent which gnawed at me. She must exhaust all the false explanations before she could resign herself to the true one. We spent monotonous evenings together, in silence or irritation; the fount of long conversations had run dry.

Ellenore decided to attract to her house various noble families who lived in her neighbourhood or at Warsaw. It was easy to see the difficulties and dangers of her attempts. The relatives who disputed her succession had divulged her past and spread all manner of calumnious reports about her. I winced at the humiliations to which she was exposing herself, and tried to dissuade her. My arguments were futile; my fears wounded her pride, although I expressed them very guardedly. She supposed that I was embarrassed by our relations, because her life was equivocal; she was only the more eager to reconquer an honourable place in society.

Her efforts were partly successful. Her wealth, her beauty which the years had barely dimmed, even her adventurous reputation—all aroused curiosity. She was soon surrounded by a numerous society, but she was haunted

91

by a secret feeling of embarrassment and uneasiness. I was unhappy at my situation, she imagined that I was unhappy at hers. She was impatient to get out of it. She was too eager to think quietly; her false position made her behaviour capricious and precipitate. Her mind was clear, but not comprehensive; and the clarity of her mind was obscured by her passionate nature, and its narrowness prevented her from seeing the wisest line and seizing the subtle nuance. Now for the first time she had a goal; because she flung herself at it, she missed it. What humiliations she swallowed without telling me! How often I blushed for her and had not the strength of mind to tell her! Such is the power of reserve and moderation over men that she was more respected as Count P———'s mistress by his friends than she was by her neighbours as the heiress to a great fortune among her own dependants. Haughty and humble by turns, now forthcoming, now hypersensitive, there was a sort of vehemence in her speech which was destructive of respect. Respect waits on calm.

In thus pointing to Ellenore's faults, I accuse and condemn myself. A word from me would have calmed her. Why could I not say the word?

Nevertheless we lived together more peaceably; distraction gave us relief from our habitual thoughts. It was only occasionally that we were alone together; and since we had boundless confidence in each other, except where our intimate feelings were concerned, we put observations and facts in the place of feelings, and our conversations regained a certain charm. But this new mode of life soon became a source of perplexity to me. Lost in the crowd surrounding Ellenore, I perceived that I was the object of astonishment and blame. Her lawsuit was coming on; her opponents contended that she had alienated her father's affections by aberrations innumerable; my presence confirmed their assertions. Her friends accused me of doing her harm. They excused her passion for me, but accused me of indelicacy: I was abusing a sentiment which I ought to have moderated. I alone knew that if I left her I should drag her after me; and that in order to follow me she would be careless of her fortune, and of all prudence besides. I could not let the public into this secret; and so in Ellenore's house I appeared only as a stranger prejudicial to the success of the case on which her fate depended. By a fantastic reversal of the truth, while I was the victim of her unshakable will, she was pitied as the victim of my domination.

Yet another circumstance came to complicate this painful situation.

There was a sudden revolution in Ellenore's conduct and manners. Up till now she seemed to be occupied with me alone; suddenly I saw her receiving and seeking the attentions of the men who surrounded her. The reserved, cold, retiring woman seemed to change her character in an instant. She encouraged the sentiments and even the hopes of a crowd of young men, some attracted by her beauty, and some serious aspirants to her hand, in spite of her past. She permitted them long tête-à-têtes. She had with them that ambiguous and seductive way which attracts by gently repelling, because it suggests indecision rather than indifference, delay more than refusal. Afterwards I learned from her (and the facts proved it to me) that her behaviour was based on a false and deplorable calculation. She thought to revive my love by exciting my jealousy; she was only poking cinders which could not be rekindled. Perhaps, without her knowing, there was a tincture of woman's vanity in her calculation! She was wounded by my coldness, and wanted to prove to herself that she was still attractive. Perhaps, too, in the loneliness in which I had left her heart, she found a sort of consolation in hearing the language of love which I had long ceased to speak.

However that may be, for some time I mistook her motives. I glimpsed the dawn of my future liberty, and rejoiced. Fearful of checking by some rash movement this crucial process on which deliverance depended, I became gentler, and appeared happier.

Ellenore took my gentleness for love, my hope
of seeing her happy at last without me for the
desire to make her happy. She congratulated
herself on her stratagem. But sometimes she
took alarm at not seeing me uneasy; and she
reproached me with not hindering relations
which apparently threatened to take her from
me. I laughed her accusations aside, but I
did not always succeed in setting her at rest;
her character showed through the dissimulation she imposed on it. The scenes began
again, in another setting, but just as stormy.
Ellenore blamed me for her own wrong-doing;
she hinted that one word would bring her back
to me entire; then, offended by my silence, in
a kind of fury she flung herself into her flirtations again.

Here more than anywhere, I feel, I shall
be accused of weakness. I wanted to be free,
and I could have been, with general approbation; perhaps I ought to have been. Ellenore's
behaviour warranted me, and seemed to compel me. But did I not know that her behaviour
was my doing? Did I not know that in her
inmost heart she had never ceased to love me?
Could I punish her for an imprudence which
I made her commit, and like a cold hypocrite,
find in her imprudence a pretext for ruthlessly
abandoning her?

Assuredly, I do not wish to excuse myself.
I condemn myself more severely than perhaps
another would in my place; but I can at least

give this sworn testimony to myself, that I have never acted on calculation, but have always been guided by true and natural feelings. How is it that with these feelings I have done nothing for so long but make myself and others unhappy?

But society watched me with surprise. My staying with Ellenore could only be explained by a profound attachment to her, but that was belied by my indifference to the ties she seemed always ready to contract. My inexplicable tolerance was attributed to light principles, to a carelessness of morality, which (they said) showed me a profoundly selfish man, corrupted by society. These conjectures were welcomed and repeated; being proportioned to the minds which conceived them, they made the more impression. They came to my ears at last. I was indignant at this unexpected discovery. My reward for my years of devotion was to be misunderstood and slandered. I had forgotten all the interests and rejected all the pleasures of life for a woman, and it was I who was condemned.

I had a heated explanation with Ellenore: at a word the crowd of adorers vanished, whom she had summoned only to make me fearful of losing her. She confined her circle to a few women and older men. Everything around us looked regular again; but we were only the more unhappy. Ellenore believed she had acquired new rights; I felt myself loaded with new chains.

I cannot describe the bitternesses and the
furies which sprang from our thus complicated
relations.    Our life was one incessant storm.
Intimacy lost all its charm, and love all its
sweetness; between us now there were not
even those transient returns of tenderness
which seem to heal for a moment incurable
wounds.    The light of the truth broke in everywhere, and to make myself understood, I made
use of the harshest and most ruthless language.
I stopped only when I saw Ellenore in tears,
and even her tears were only a burning lava
which, falling drop by drop on my heart,
forced cries from me, but never a disavowal.
Then, more than once, I saw her rise, pale and
prophetic.    "Adolphe!" she cried, "you do
not know the evil you do; you will learn one
day, you will learn it from me, when you have
driven me to the grave."

Woe is me that I did not, when she spoke,
cast myself into the grave before her!

# CHAPTER IX

I had not called on Baron T——— since my first visit. One day I received the following note from him.

"The advice I gave you did not deserve that you should stay away so long. Whatever may be your attitude to your own concerns, you are still the son of my dearest friend, I should still enjoy your company, and I should be delighted to introduce you to a group of friends whose society, I can promise, will be agreeable to you. Allow me to add that the more peculiar your mode of life (which I do not wish to condemn) the more important it is for you to dispel ill-founded prejudices by showing yourself in the world."

I was grateful for the old man's kindness. I went to see him. There was no talk of Ellenore. He kept me to dinner. The company consisted of a few intelligent and amiable men. I was embarrassed at first, but I pulled myself together; I was animated, I talked; I made the most of my intelligence and my knowledge. I saw that I had succeeded in winning approval. In this success my self-esteem found a pleasure it had not known for a long time; and the pleasure made Baron T———'s society the more agreeable.

I visited him frequently. He gave me various jobs connected with his mission which he could safely entrust to me. At first Ellenore was surprised by this change in my life; but I spoke to her of the Baron's friendship with my father, and the pleasure I took in making amends to my father for my absence, by appearing to do something useful. Poor Ellenore —I feel remorse as I write it now—felt happier because I seemed calmer, and resigned herself, without complaining much, to often passing the greater part of the day without me. On his side, as soon as a little confidence was re-established between us, the Baron broached the subject of Ellenore again. I was firmly determined to speak always well of her, but imperceptibly my tone became lighter and more careless. Sometimes I showed, by general remarks, that I recognised the necessity of breaking with her; sometimes I had recourse to flippancy: I laughed about women and the difficulty of getting rid of them. This talk amused the old diplomat, whose tired soul vaguely recalled that in its youth it also had been tormented by love-intrigues. So, by the mere fact that my sentiment was concealed, I more or less deceived everybody: I deceived Ellenore, because I knew that the Baron wanted to get me away from her, and I did not tell her; I deceived the Baron because I allowed him to hope that I was ready to break with her. This duplicity was quite alien to my nature; but a man degenerates when he has one single thought in his heart which he is continually forced to dissimulate.

Hitherto, at the Baron's, I had only met his private circle of friends. One day he invited me to stay for a grand reception he was giving for the Elector's birthday. " You will meet," he said, " the loveliest women in Poland. It is true you will not find your lady among them. I am sorry. But there are women whom one can meet only at their homes." The phrase was painful. I kept silence, but inwardly I reproached myself for not defending Ellenore. If I had been attacked in her presence, she would have defended me passionately.

The company was large. They examined me carefully. I heard them whispering my father's name, Ellenore's, the Count P———'s. They stopped when I came near; they began as I went away. Obviously, they were telling my story, each in his own version. My position was unbearable. There was a cold sweat on my forehead. I reddened and went pale by turns.

The Baron noticed my embarrassment. He came to me, redoubled his attentions and courtesies, took every occasion to sing my praises, and the influence of his attitude soon made the others show me the same consideration.

When the guests had departed, the Baron said to me: " I want to talk to you again, man to man. Why do you remain in this painful situation? What good do you do to anyone? Do you think people do not know what goes on between Ellenore and yourself? Everybody knows of your mutual bitterness and discontent. You wrong yourself by your weakness, and equally by your harshness. The contradiction is fantastic. The woman makes you unhappy, and you do not make her happy."

I was still smarting from my painful experience. The Baron showed me several letters from my father. They showed him much more upset than I had supposed. I was thoroughly shaken. The idea that I was prolonging Ellenore's unhappiness added to my irresolution. At last, as though everything were united against her, while I was wavering she, by her impetuosity, decided me.

I had been away all day; the Baron had detained me after the reception; it was already late at night. A letter from Ellenore was handed to me in the Baron's presence. I could see in his eyes a sort of pity for my slavery. Ellenore's letter was full of bitterness. "Good God!" I said to myself. "I cannot pass a day in freedom. I cannot breathe an hour in peace. She pursues me everywhere, like a slave who must be brought to her feet." I was conscious of my own weakness, and was the more violent. "Yes," I cried, "I will give you my promise— to break with Ellenore. I will tell her myself. You can write to tell my father in advance."

I rushed away from the Baron. My own words oppressed me, and I only half believed in the promise I had given.

Ellenore was waiting impatiently for me. By a strange chance, during my absence, some-one had told her for the first time of the Baron's efforts to get me away from her. She had been told of my conversations and my flippant remarks. Her suspicions were aroused, and she had gathered together various circum-stances which seemed to confirm them. My sudden intimacy with a man whom formerly I never saw, the close relation between him and my father, were certain proofs to her. Her anxiety had increased so much in a few hours that I found her completely convinced of what she called my perfidy.

I had come to her, decided to tell all. But when I found myself accused by her—can you believe it?—my one concern was to evade everything. I even denied, yes, I denied to-day what I was determined to tell her to-morrow.

It was late. I left her. I hurried to bed to end this interminable day; and when I was quite certain it was over, I felt for a moment relieved of a monstrous burden.

I did not get up till near midday, as though by postponing the beginning of our interview, I had postponed the fatal moment.

During the night Ellenore had been re-assured, by her own thoughts and by what I had said the night before. She spoke of her affairs with a confidence which told me plainly that she regarded our lives as indissolubly united. How was I to find the words that would condemn her to loneliness again?

The time was passing with frightening speed. Every minute made more urgent the necessity of an explanation. Of the three days I had fixed, the second had nearly gone. The Baron expected me at latest the day after to-morrow. His letter to my father had been sent off, and I was going to fail my promise without having made the faintest attempt to perform it. I left the room, I came back again, I took Ellenore's hand, I began a phrase and abruptly broke off. I watched the sun descend towards the horizon. Another night came, and another postponement. One day remained. An hour would have been enough.

That day passed like the one before. I wrote to the Baron to ask for more time, and, as weak characters naturally are, I was prodigal of reasons to justify my delay, to prove that it meant no change in the decision I had taken, and that from now on it could be taken for granted that I had broken for ever with Ellenore.

# CHAPTER X

I was calmer during the following days. The necessity of action had become indefinite; it no longer pursued me like a spectre; I thought I had plenty of time to prepare Ellenore. I wanted to be gentler and more tender with her, so as to preserve at least the memory of our love. My trouble was now quite different from what it had been before. I had prayed heaven that an impassable barrier should suddenly come between Ellenore and me. The barrier was now there. I looked at Ellenore as on a being I was going to lose. Her exigence, which had so often seemed intolerable, no longer frightened me; I felt my freedom in advance. In giving way to her now I felt freer; and I experienced no more of the inward rebellion which in the past incessantly impelled me to tear everything to pieces. There was no more impatience in me; on the contrary, there was a secret desire to put off the fatal moment.

Ellenore noticed this increase of affection and tenderness, and became less bitter. Now I sought the conversations I had avoided; now I took delight in her words of love, which had irritated me before: now they were precious; each one of them might be the last.

One evening we parted after a conversation sweeter than usual. The secret I kept in my bosom saddened me; but my sadness was

calm. The uncertainty in which I had contrived to wrap the time of separation served
to keep the idea of it away. During the night
I heard an unfamiliar noise in the château. It
was soon over, and I thought no more about it.
But in the morning I remembered it, and
wanted to know the cause. I went towards
Ellenore's room. I was astounded to be told
that for the last twelve hours she had been in
a burning fever, that a doctor summoned by
her household said her life was in danger, and
that she had given the strictest orders that I
was not to be told or allowed to see her.

I wanted to insist. The doctor himself
came out to explain the necessity of sparing
her any emotion. He did not know the reason
for her orders, but he attributed them to her
desire not to alarm me. In anguish, I questioned her servants to find out what could have
plunged her so suddenly into such a dangerous
condition.

The evening before, after leaving me, a
man on horse-back had brought her a letter
from Warsaw. She opened it, read it, and
fainted. When she came to herself, she threw
herself on her bed without a word. One of her
maids, worried by her mistress's agitation,
stayed in her room unperceived. Towards mid-
night, she saw her mistress seized by a fit of
trembling which shook the bed on which she
lay. The maid wanted to call me. But Ellenore
forbade it in a kind of terror, so violent that

she dared not disobey. A doctor was sent for. But Ellenore had refused—still refused—to answer his questions. She had passed the night, murmuring broken words which they could not understand, often pressing her handkerchief to her mouth, as though to prevent herself from speaking.

While they were giving me these details another maid who had remained with Ellenore, rushed up in a fright. Ellenore appeared to be losing consciousness. She could distinguish nothing in her surroundings. Sometimes she uttered a cry; she repeated my name; then, terrified, she signed with her hand as though beseeching that some hateful object should be removed.

I entered her room. I saw two letters at the foot of the bed. One was mine to the Baron, the other from himself to Ellenore. I understood only too well the clue to the fearful enigma. All my efforts to gain the time I wanted to devote to our last farewells had turned against the unhappy woman I wished to spare. Ellenore had read, in my own hand, my promises to leave her—promises dictated by my desire to stay with her a little longer, promises which the extremity of this very desire had made me repeat and elaborate. The Baron's objective eye had easily read in these repeated protestations the irresolution which I tried to disguise, the ruses of my own uncertainty; but the cruel man had calculated, only too well, that Ellenore would see in them an irrevocable sentence.

I came close to her. She looked at me, but did not recognise me. I spoke to her; she started. "What is that noise?" she cried. "It is the voice which has hurt me." The doctor saw that my presence increased her delirium, and begged me to go away. How describe what I felt for three long hours? At last the doctor came out. Ellenore had fallen into a deep sleep. He did not despair of saving her if the fever had abated when she woke.

Ellenore slept a long while. When I heard that she was awake, I wrote to ask her to see me. She sent word that I could come. I began to speak; she interrupted me. "Do not say one cruel word," she said. "I make no more claims; I oppose nothing. But do not let the voice I have loved so much, the voice which echoed in the depths of my heart, enter it now to tear it to pieces. Adolphe, Adolphe! I have been violent; I may have wounded you; but you do not know what I have suffered. God grant you never will!"

Her agitation became extreme. She leaned her forehead on my hand; it was burning; her features were terribly contorted. "In heaven's name, dear Ellenore," I cried, "listen to me. Yes, I am guilty: that letter . . ." She shuddered, and tried to move away. I held her back. I went on. "Weak, tortured, I may have yielded for a moment to a cruel pressure;

but have you not yourself a thousand proofs that I cannot will our separation? I have been discontented, unhappy, unjust. Perhaps, by struggling too violently against my rebel imagination, you have given strength to passing wishes which I despise to-day. But can you doubt the depth of my affection? Are not our souls chained to each other by countless unbreakable bonds? Do we not share all the past? Can we look at the three years which have just ended without recalling the feelings we have shared, the delights we have known, the pains we have borne together? Ellenore, let us begin a new life to-day; let us call back the times of happiness and love."

She looked at me a while, with an air of doubt. "Your father," she said at last. "Your duty, your family—what is expected of you . ."

"Some time, I suppose," I replied, "one day perhaps . . ."

She noticed my hesitation. "My God!" she cried. "Why did he give me back hope only to snatch it away again? Adolphe, I thank you for your efforts. They have done me good—the more good because they will not cost you any sacrifice, I hope. But I beg of you, let us speak no more of the future . . . Do not reproach yourself with anything, whatever happens. You have been good to me. I wanted the impossible. Love was all my life: it could not be all yours. Take care of me a few days longer." Tears poured from her eyes; she breathed a little more freely; she leaned her head on my shoulder. " Here," she said, " I always wanted to die."

I pressed her to my heart; again I abjured my plans, and disavowed my cruel angers. " No," she said, " you must be free and contented."

" How can I be, if you are unhappy?"

" I shall not be unhappy long; you will not have long to be sorry for me."

I thrust away the fears that I wanted to believe imaginary.

" No, no, dear Adolphe," she said, " when we have cried for death a long while, heaven sends us at last a sure presentiment that our prayer is granted."

I swore to her that I would never leave her.

" I always hoped it, now I am certain of it."

It was one of those winter days when the sun sadly lights the grey countryside, as though he looked with pity on the earth he has ceased to warm. Ellenore proposed that we should go out.

" It is very cold," I said.

" No matter. I want to go for a walk with you."

She took my arm; we walked for a long time in silence; she moved forward with difficulty, leaning nearly all her weight on me.

" Let us stop for a moment."

"No," she answered. "I love to feel myself still supported by you."

We were silent again. The sky was serene, but the trees were leafless. Not a breath moved the air, not a bird flew through it. Everything was motionless; and the only sound was the crunching of the frozen grass under our feet.

"How calm everything is!" Ellenore said to me. "How nature is resigned! Ought not the heart also learn to be resigned?"

She sat down on a stone; suddenly she sank on to her knees and bent her head, leaning it on her two hands. I heard her murmur some words. I saw she was praying. At last she got up. "Let us go back," she said. "The cold has caught me. I am afraid I may be ill. Do not say anything to me; I am not in a state to understand."

From that day on, I watched Ellenore grow weaker and waste away. I summoned doctors from all parts to her. Some told me it was an incurable disease; others lulled me with vain hopes; but dark silent nature pursued its pitiless work with invisible hands. There were moments when Ellenore seemed to recover life. Sometimes one would have said that the iron hand which pressed her down was withdrawn. She lifted her languid head; the colour on her cheeks was a little livelier; there was animation in her eyes. But suddenly by the cruel game of an unknown power

110

this deceptive improvement disappeared, art could not discover why. Thus I watched her move forward step by step to destruction. I saw the signs of coming death engrave themselves on her noble and expressive face. It was lamentable and humiliating to see her proud and fiery character confusedly and incoherently impressed by bodily suffering, as though in these terrible moments, the soul, galled by the body, was being totally changed in order to accommodate itself less painfully to the organic degradation.

But one sentiment was unchanging in Ellenore's heart: her tenderness for me. She was so weak that she could rarely speak to me; but she silently fixed her eyes on me, and it seemed to me then that her eyes were asking me for the life I could no longer give. I was frightened of causing her strong emotion; I invented excuses for going out: I wandered aimlessly through the places where I had been with her; I shed tears on the stones, the feet of the trees, everything that brought back her memory to me.

It was not regret for love; the feeling was sadder and more sombre than that. Love is so utterly identified with the beloved object that even in its despair there is a certain magic. It struggles against reality, against destiny; its passionate desire deceives it about its powers, and exalts it in the midst of its pain. My pain was dull and solitary; I had no hope of dying with Ellenore; I was to live without her in this desert of the world, which I had so often longed to travel through alone. I had broken the heart which loved me, my own heart's mate, the heart which had persisted in devotion to me, in indefatigable tenderness. Isolation gripped me already. Ellenore was still breathing, but I could no longer confide my thoughts to her. I was already alone on the earth, I lived no more in that atmosphere of love which she spread round me; the air I breathed seemed harsher, the faces I met more indifferent. All nature seemed to be saying to me that I was going to cease to be loved—for ever.

Suddenly, Ellenore's danger became more imminent; unmistakable symptoms announced that the end was near. A priest of her religion broke it to her. She begged me to bring her a box which contained many papers. She had some of them burned in her presence; but she seemed to be looking for one which she could not find, and her distress was extreme. I besought her to give up the agitating search; she had fainted twice already.

"Very well," she replied. "But you must grant me this one prayer, dear Adolphe. You will find among my papers somewhere a letter addressed to you. Burn it without reading it, I beseech you in the name of our love, in the name of these last moments which you have soothed."

I gave my promise; and she was at peace. " Now let me give myself to the duties of religion. I have many sins to expiate. Perhaps my love for you was a sin. But I should not believe it, if my love could have made you happy."

I left her. I returned only with her household to participate in the last solemn prayers. On my knees in a corner of her room, now I plunged into the abyss of my own thoughts, now I watched with unwilling curiosity all these people gathered together—the terror of some, the heedlessness of others, and that strange effect of habit which brings indifference into all prescribed rites, and makes the most august and awful ceremonies to be regarded as matters of course and pure form. I heard them mechanically repeat the words of death, as though they themselves would never be actors in a like scene, as though they would never have to die. Nevertheless, I was far from despising these practices. Is there a single one of them which man, in his ignorance, can dare to pronounce useless? They brought calm to Ellenore; they helped her to pass those awful straits towards which we all are journeying, and none of us can say what he will experience then. I am not surprised that man needs a religion: what astonishes me is that he should ever believe himself strong enough, or immune enough from misfortune, to dare reject any of them. I should have thought that, in his weakness, he would be impelled to invoke them all. In the darkness that surrounds us can we afford to reject a single gleam? In the torrent which sweeps us away is there a single branch that we can dare not to grasp?

The impression produced on Ellenore by this mournful solemnity seemed to have tired her. She was overcome by a fairly deep and peaceful sleep; she woke with less pain. I was alone in her room. We spoke from time to time, at long intervals. The doctor whose guesses had been cleverest had told me that she would not live another twenty-four hours. I looked in turns at the clock, and at Ellenore's face, on which I saw no new change. Every minute that passed reawakened hope, and I once more doubted the prognostications of the deceitful art. Suddenly, Ellenore started forward. I held her back. Her whole body was shaking convulsively. Her eyes sought me; but in her eyes was a vague fear, as though she cried for mercy from something threatening which I could not see. She raised herself, she fell back; I saw she was trying to escape. It was as though she were struggling against some invisible physical power which, weary of waiting, had seized her and now held her down on the death-bed to despatch her. At last she yielded to the ruthless enmity of nature; her limbs collapsed; she seemed to regain a little consciousness: she clasped my hand; she would weep, but there were no more tears; she would speak, but there was no more voice; as though resigned, she let her head fall on the arm which held it up; her breathing grew slower. In a few moments, she was dead.

I stayed a long while motionless beside the lifeless Ellenore. The conviction of her death had not yet penetrated my soul; my eyes stared in stupid astonishment at the lifeless body. One of her women entered, and spread the grim news through the house. The noise about me woke me from the lethargy in which I was plunged. I got up. And then I felt the tearing pain and all the horror of the irrevocable goodbye. All the movement and activity of vulgar life, all the cares and agitations which had nothing to do with her, scattered the illusion to which I clung, the illusion of believing I still existed with Ellenore. I felt the last bond break, and the frightful reality interpose for ever between her and me. How it crushed me down—the liberty which I had so longed for! How my heart hungered for the dependence which had often made me rebel! Then, all my actions had an end; I was certain, by each one of them, of sparing a pain or giving a pleasure. Then, I complained of it; I was irritated that a loving eye watched my doings, and that another's happiness was knit up with them. No one watched them now; they interested nobody; no one disputed with me for my time—my hours; no voice called me back when I went out. I was free,

indeed; I was no longer loved; I was a stranger
to all the world.

They brought me all Ellenore's papers, as
she had ordered.   In every line I found new
proofs of her love, new sacrifices that she had
made for me, and hidden from me.   At last
I found the letter I had promised to burn;
I did not recognise it at first; it had no
address, and it was open.   Some words caught
my eye in spite of myself.   I tried in vain to
turn my eyes away, I could not resist the craving to read it all.   I have not the strength to
copy it.   Ellenore had written it after one
of the violent scenes before her illness.

"Adolphe, (she wrote) why are you so
ruthless against me?   What is my crime?
That I love you, that I cannot exist without
you?   What is this strange pity which makes
you afraid to break a bond which oppresses
you, and makes you destroy the unhappy being
whom your pity will not let you leave?   Why
do you deny me the sad pleasure of believing
that you are at least generous?   Why are you
angry and weak?   The idea of my unhappiness
haunts you, but the sight of it cannot stop you!
What do you want of me?   That I should leave
you?   Do you not see that I have not the
strength?   Ah! it is for you, who do not love
—it is for you to find the strength, in a heart
grown tired of me, which all my love has been
unable to disarm.   But you will not give it
me; you will make me pine away with weeping,

you will make me die at your feet."

"Speak the word," she wrote again. "Is there a country where I will not follow you? Is there a hiding place where I will not bury myself to live near you; without being a burden on your life? But no, you will not have it. All the plans I put forward, timid and trembling, (for you have frozen me with fear) you reject impatiently. The best I get from you is silence. Such cruelty is foreign to your character. You are good; your actions are noble and devoted. But what actions can wipe away your words? Those cutting words echo round me; I hear them at night; they follow me, they gnaw at me, they blight everything you do. Must I die then, Adolphe? Well, you will be satisfied. She will die—the poor creature you protected, but whom you strike again and again. She will die—the troublesome Ellenore whom you cannot bear to be near you, whom you look on as an obstacle, for whom you cannot find a spot on earth that does not weary you. She will die: you will walk alone in the midst of the crowd you are impatient to join. You will come to know them—these men to whom you are now grateful for their indifference. And perhaps one day, when you are wounded by these unfeeling hearts, you will regret the heart of which you were the lord, which lived on your affection, which would have braved every danger to defend you, and which you no longer deign to reward with a look."

# LETTER TO THE EDITOR

Sir, I am returning the manuscript which you were kind enough to lend me. I thank you for the favour, although it has revived sad memories which time had obliterated. I knew most of the people in this story, which is only too true. I often saw the eccentric and unhappy Adolphe, who is the author and hero; I tried by my advice to rescue the charming Ellenore, who deserved a gentler fate and a more faithful heart, from the malign being who, as unhappy as she, dominated her by a sort of spell and tore her to pieces by his weakness. Alas, the last time I saw her, I believed I had given her some strength, and had armed her reason against her heart. But I was too long away, and when I returned where I had left her, I found only a grave.

You ought to publish the narrative. It cannot wound anyone now, and I think it will do some good. The tragedy of Ellenore proves that the most passionate sentiment cannot struggle against the order of things. Society is too powerful, too protean; it mixes too much bitterness with a love it does not sanction; it seconds the inclination to inconstancy and the impatient fatigue—those diseases of the soul which sometimes seize it in the midst of intimacy. The indifferent show a marvellous enthusiasm for making mischief in the name of morality and doing harm by their zeal for virtue; it is as though the sight of love offends them, because they are incapable of it; and when they can find a pretext, they delight to attack and destroy it. Unhappy the woman who rests on a sentiment which everything conspires to poison, and against which society, when it is not compelled to recognise it as legitimate, arms itself with all that is bad in the human heart to discourage all that is good in it.

Adolphe's example will be even more instructive if you add that, after rejecting the being who loved him, he was just as disquieted, as agitated, as malcontent as before; that he made no use of the freedom he reconquered at the cost of such tears and pain; and that in making us blame him, he has also made us pity him.

If you want proof, read these letters which will tell you of Adolphe's fate. You will see him in many different circumstances, but always the victim of that mixture of egotism and sensibility which combined in him to make him and others wretched; foreseeing the evil before he does it, shrinking back in despair after it is done; punished by his qualities even more than his defects, because his qualities derived from his emotions and not from his principles; by turns, the most devoted and the hardest of men, but always ending with hardness after beginning with devotion, and thus leaving behind no traces save those of the wrongs he had done.

# REPLY.

Sir, Yes, I shall publish the manuscript you have returned to me—not that I share your opinion on its usefulness: in this world people learn only by experience, and every woman who reads it will imagine she has found something better than Adolphe, or that she is better than Ellenore—but I shall publish it as a true story of the misery of the human heart. If it contains an instructive lesson, the lesson is for men: it proves that the intellect they are so proud of, avails neither to find happiness nor to give it; it proves that character, strength, fidelity, goodness are gifts they must ask from heaven: and I do not call goodness that passing pity which does not subdue impatience, nor prevent it from reopening the wounds which a moment of regret had closed. The great problem in life is the suffering we cause, and the most ingenious metaphysic does not justify the man who has lacerated the heart which loved him. Besides, I detest the imbecility of a mind which believes it has excused what it has explained; I detest the vanity which is pre-occupied with itself while recounting the harm it has done, which claims to arouse our sympathy in describing itself, which rises indestructible from the ruins and analyses itself instead of repenting. I detest the weakness which always blames others for its own impotence, and does not see that the evil is not in its surroundings, but in itself. I should have guessed that Adolphe would have been punished for his character by his character itself, that he had followed no fixed path, pursued no useful career, and wasted his faculties, guided only by caprice and impelled only by irritation. I should have guessed all that, I say, even if you had not given me fresh details about his fate. I do not know whether I shall make use of them. Circumstances count for little, character is everything; it is useless to break with things and persons, if you cannot break with yourself. You change the situation; but you carry into every new one the torment from which you hoped to be delivered; and since you never change yourself by changing scene, you find you have only added remorse to regret and sin to suffering.

# PART II

# CHAPTER I

*Adolphe* is a deeply moving story; it is also
a penetrating analysis of the psychology of
love. It would not, indeed, be the former
unless it were also the latter. One is persuaded
that it tells the truth—the subtle truth—of an
important human situation: the relation of
two human souls which have indeed " en-
countered " one another. Nothing is suffered
to distract us from the encounter of souls. One
looks back and is almost astonished to realise
that there has been hardly a word of physical
description of the man or the woman.
Ellenore's physical surrender is described in a
single phrase of six words. It is a story of
love, as the relation between two souls.

I am no Platonicist; neither were Adolphe
and Ellenore. But it is axiomatic in their story
that love of the body attends on love of the
soul; it is the outward and sensible sign of the
inward and spiritual grace. This may be old-
fashioned doctrine nowadays; but it is the true
one. And if it is equally old-fashioned to proclaim that there is a true doctrine in such
matters, it is nevertheless the doctrine by
which some men and women still elect to live.

Love is a relation between two souls.
What is the nature of this relation? Primarily
and essentially it is a relation of absolute trust.
The trust is entire. It is a mutual and complete
self-surrender, which is also a mutual and com-

125

plete gift of liberty. They do not know what love is, who have not experienced in it a freedom of another order, a different dimension from the condition which usually bears the name of freedom. Love is the relation, and the only one, in which we are at last free to be ourselves.

By this standard there is only one true lover in the story: and that is Ellenore. Adolphe has only the illusion of love. There is a fatal element of vanity in him which poisons his relation from the beginning. He wants to add the experience of love to his accomplishments; he wants to make a conquest worthy of himself—of his distinguished, lonely and misunderstood soul. It is primarily the disturbance due to the thwarting of his vanity, the emotional upheaval caused by the threat of disaster to his self-esteem when Ellenore at first dismisses him, which he mistakes for love. She also mistakes it for love; and in return for his imagined love, she loves indeed. He cannot live without her, he cries; and it is not untrue. But what cannot live, what is threatened with death, or rather mortification, is his conception of himself. But when she cries that she cannot live without him, it is a total truth. Without him, she dies indeed. The whole of her has been surrendered, and it craves the whole of him. But the whole of him does not exist. Love, which might have brought it to birth, has passed him by, powerless to gain an

entry through his carapace of self-concern. All
that he really has to give is pity; and this pity
is not for her. It is his own shrinking from the
pain caused him by her pain. He tells himself
that he shrinks from hurting her; but it is his
own pain that frightens him. Had he the fortitude to endure that, one feels, the wound in
Ellenore's heart could have healed. It would
have left a permanent scar, but it would have
healed.

So Adolphe becomes to Ellenore like a pur-
suing Fury, sensitive and implacable. In every
sense of the phrase he cannot leave her alone:
yet he cannot unite himself to her. More truly,
he cannot leave her alone, because he cannot
unite himself to her. By a dreadful but natural
perversity, he cannot tear himself away from
the suffering he causes her. And, on her side,
it is not her love, but the lack of love in him,
which makes her crave so hungrily for his
presence, and become incapable of letting him
go. The love which fills her demands nothing
better, nothing so much, as to trust. But she
cannot trust him. It is beyond her power; it
is impossible. She has but one desire: to give
him the freedom of love. But it is not in her
power to do so, because it depends on the birth
of love in him. Were she secure of that, then
she could give him the freedom of love. He
could go away, pursue his man's concerns,
make a name and fame for himself, and her
heart would be at rest. She would not be cheer-

ful at his absences—no loving woman can be
that—but she would not suffer; she would be
assured of the happiness of return and
reunion.

The fatal element of vanity in Adolphe
has various manifestations: of which the most
devastating and disastrous is the vanity which
was the original motive of his paying court to
Ellenore—the desire to prove to himself that
he can make a conquest of the rarest woman
of his acquaintance. It is also manifest in the
desire to be of account in the society he affects
to despise, and which part of him genuinely
does despise. He has not the strength of
character to brave the conventions of whose
superficiality he is convinced, because his vanity
cannot contemplate becoming a social outcast.
Constant makes plain enough his own
conviction that, if Adolphe had had the
strength of character, he would eventually have
conquered a place for them both in the world.
The Count and Ellenore have already done so,
she by her devotion, he by his courage,
although there is lacking to their relation the
fullness of love. And Adolphe himself declares:
"I am convinced that if I had loved Ellenore,
I should have won opinion over to her and me.
Such is the power of true feeling that, when
it speaks, false interpretations and artificial
conventions are dumb."

That may be thought a romantic view.
Possibly it is; but the adjective is unimportant

provided the view is true. Constant believed it was, and so do I. The root of the trouble was that Adolphe did not love Ellenore, and that it was his vanity which prevented him.

But vanity is not perhaps the most illuminating word in such a case; it is certainly not entirely fair to Adolphe. Adolphe speaks the truth when he describes the birth of his new craving for a liaison which would flatter his self-esteem.

> No doubt there was a good deal of vanity in this craving, but it was not only vanity; and perhaps there was less than I myself believed. A man's sentiments are confused and mixed; they are composed of a multitude of various feelings which cannot be observed. Words, always too clumsy and general, may serve to indicate them; but they can never define them.

Indeed, if we consider the whole tenour of the story, we shall find that what Adolphe suffered from was not so much what is commonly called vanity as a fundamental insecurity in his own being: the lack of the simple certainty that he was he. He felt that he needed the recognition of others to give him some assurance of his own " solidity " and value. It was a delusion, for no convincing assurance of the kind required can be had that way. Neither the approbation of the world nor even the love of a woman can effect the subtle change. In the eyes of this basic self-mistrust they appear to be too easily won. The person who is approved, admired or loved, has only a shadowy and equivocal existence: he is a kind of *sosie*, perched on one's back, whom one can never see face to face.

I do not know whether this dislocation of the self is a common condition. It may not be apparent in those more happily constituted natures which glide smoothly into a groove in society and have a sort of identity conferred on them by the complex of social relations in which they are enmeshed.  They take their place, and their place is a mould which impresses them with a shape they feel to be their own.  Or one might say they crystallise themselves about the point in the social world they are called to occupy.  They are immune from the radical sense of discrepancy between themselves and any fixed situation which haunts and bewilders the young man who lacks the conviction of his own indefeasible identity.

To this latter kind of men, whether rare or common, Adolphe (and the youthful Constant behind him) certainly belonged.  By what seems, to a maturer view, a strange paradox, while they are entirely uncertain of the nature and even of the reality of their own " proper self," they are inordinately sensitive to any encroachment upon it.  But, obviously, the " self " of which they resent any invasion is a kind of figment.  Nevertheless, the feeling that it must be safeguarded against invasion is incontrovertible and overwhelming.  It would appear then that the " self " which they are so nervous to defend is, in fact, a notional concept of freedom as unlimited potentiality. What they dread, apparently, is commitment: the choice which is irrevocable, as all real choices are. But so equally is the refusal to make a choice.

Is the condition then simply one of wavering between conscious and unconscious commitment? It may be so to the eye of remote analysis; but that does not correspond with the actual experience of the condition. And anyhow unconscious commitment is a psychological paradox. The extravagant clinging to a notional freedom, the agitated effort to escape the commitment which presents itself as an irreparable loss of liberty, springs directly from the sense that there is nothing in one which *can* choose. A dim presentiment warns one that choice must be the act of the whole man, an expression of the total being. This presentiment is vague, if only because wholeness and integrity of being is merely a notional condition—or, at best, a possibility revealed by the acute awareness that any actual or imminent choice could have only a part of the self behind it. Behind, or implicit in, the feverish defence of the self as unlimited potentiality and the frenzied resistance to commitment, is the perception of another paradox: that to a valid choice there are no alternatives.

This felt necessity of a valid choice is, of course, a subjective impression. Whether it corresponds to some necessary connection in objective reality is a question to which the intellect as such can give no valid answer. It cannot deny it; but it cannot affirm it either. But the felt necessity of a valid choice is immensely important for human living. It is the psychological or spiritual happening which underlies what religion describes as doing the will of God. And, whatever may be our theological beliefs, the religious description is appropriate to the experience. There is a supersession of the personal will, which falls as it were into abeyance. Apparently *we* cannot will the choice made by our total being. And that seems natural enough, for we are conscious of will as a power at our disposal which can be thrown behind one of a number of alternative choices of action. Choices and will appear to be correlative, and dependent on each other for their existnce. But what I have hurriedly called a valid choice, and had better call an integral decision, admits no alternatives and therefore allows the will no opportunity to manifest itself. By the same token it allows no manifestation of the personal self which, at any rate in ordinary language, is correlative to will and choices. The familiar " I " is that which wills, and is conscious of itself in the act of willing which is exercised in choosing among alternative courses of action.

This is not to suggest that a life can be composed of integral decisions: though I sup-

pose that, looked at from this angle, the life
of the religious recluse is an effort to avoid
diversion from the path of an integral decision.
But for more ordinary people integral decision
is something which happens, if it happens at
all, only in crucial moments of their lives, when
the main lines of the pattern are decided. The
texture is still composed of choice and will and
the activities of the familiar " I ". But, of
course, this texture will differ from the texture of the life in which integral decision has
played no part: because the texture will at
least follow the lines of the pattern which has
been endorsed by the total being. On the other
hand the texture of a life without integral decision will follow a pattern which has been imposed by external influences.

The metaphor, as all metaphors must be
in this realm, is partly misleading. For the
experience of integral decision introduces a
dominant in the life-process. Its novelty and
compulsiveness is such that in the future it
demands to be waited for. It is as though no
truly important and meaningful decision can
be made without it; and a decision must be
either integral or indifferent. That may be
roughly the fact. The impetus of an integral
decision carries one a long way, its consequences flow naturally or, as we may say, inevitably, for a very long while. It is quite possible that religion comes nearest the truth of
the matter when it insists that there is in fact

only one integral decision in a human life: namely, whether to submit to God or not. That rings true. The difficulties, the dangers and the disputes arise from dogmatic assertions about the nature of God, and in particular about His commands.

Provisionally we may suppose that God is experienced in a moment of integral decision. At any rate, by this hypothesis we obtain the use of a language which is appropriate to the phenomenon. For the most impressive characteristic of a moment of integral decision is that the decision is not our own, in the ordinary sense; yet it is made in us and for us, and in the making of it we come to be more ourselves than we ever were before. We are, for the first time, our true selves; and the true self is quite incommensurable with any self we were conscious of before. Since the change we experience is from division into unity, this seems natural enough: for unity is generically different from multiplicity. If the integral being is the true self, they are specious selves which inhabit the divided being. The tension and conflict between them disappears: they are merged, and changed in the process of merging, into a new whole. You may explain this supra-personal self as God taking possession of the human being; or you may explain it as the irruption of the life-force, asserting itself against the condition of stasis produced by inward division. But by one way or another, if you try faithfully to describe it, you will be introducing something indistinguishable from the concept of God.   If you use Occam's razor to cut this out, you will find you have killed the experience itself.

# CHAPTER II

We return to the story of Adolphe and
Ellenore. By the criterion we have established, Adolphe does not experience God:
Ellenore does. That will not suit the book of
what is often called Christian morality. But
this brand of Christian morality is not very
religious: in fact, hardly religious at all. It
is mainly a sanction for social conventions.
Ellenore's life is one long offence against them.
Nevertheless, she is an exceptionally good and
noble woman, who fulfils herself in love. When
the moment of integral decision comes to her
she responds entirely. God takes possession
of her and never lets her go. Her love is disastrous to her, in worldly terms: nevertheless,
it is her salvation. And Constant is quite
right to make her a naturally Christian soul,
even a pious one; but whose piety has the
purity of its original source. She does not
admit that her love for Adolphe was a sin.
" Perhaps it was," she says on her deathbed to
Adolphe, " but I should not believe it if my
love could have made you happy." The only
thing that makes Ellenore dubious of her love
is its impotence to make her beloved happy.
The attitude is true to the nature of a noble
and natural woman. The offence against the
conventions counts for nothing, as indeed it
is nothing on the plane on which Ellenore is
trying to judge herself. She is concerned with

how her soul stands to God—not the conventional, but the eternal one. She knows (as we know) the purity and faithfulness of her heart; she knows how completely she had surrendered herself to God when He visited her. Why has her love not made her lover happy? The thought that it has failed to do so because her love was sinful never finds lodgment in her mind. That it seems even to enter it is only a subterfuge of speech, because she desires to spare him the truth; just as she makes him promise to burn the letter in which, in a moment of agony, she had told him the truth.

Her love could not make him happy because he was weak. He was too weak to surrender himself to love. It was not strength but its opposite, which impelled him to cling to the spurious freedom of non-commitment, to keep open a way of escape, to guard jealously the citadel of his own ego, to avoid the plunge into the waters of Lethe, to shrink from the dreadful risk of rebirth. That is not to imply that if he could have taken the plunge, life would have become plain sailing for them both. But he would have tasted the *vita nuova*. A new value, a new criterion, the knowledge of a new dimension of existence, would have entered his life. To follow the new star, to be loyal to the new life, would assuredly have cost him months, and probably years, of struggle. He would have had to fight for his new strength, to contend with the ambitions

and affections which would impair his loyalty
to his woman and his fidelity to the God who
had united them.   But every struggle would
have ended in a step upward on the road
towards wholeness and mutual devotion and
more abundant life, instead of a step down-
ward towards deeper division and mutual destruction and death.

Adolphe ventured only part of himself into
the experience of love.   He was determined on
this from the beginning.   He wanted not love,
but the experience of love—something of
which his future " I ", consubstantial with and
unchanged from the " I " of the present and
past, could say proudly or complacently " I
have experienced this."   The ego would
emerge intact; it must emerge intact.   Those
were the terms on which he entered the encounter which he deliberately sought.   Yet they
made impossible the liberation from the ego
which is the condition and consequence of love.
Love cannot be experienced as he was resolved
to experience it : for it is a surrender of the ego
in a blessed and beneficent exchange for something different.

It is easy to condemn Adolphe.   But how
difficult it is for the self-conscious and sensitive man to entertain, even as an intellectual
possibility, the idea of the reality of love!   It
is so revolutionary.   It turns upside down what
he has come to regard as the laws of his own

being, and obliterates what he thinks the indispensable conditions of his personal existence. Indeed, a just intellectual conception of love, prior to any experience of it, would seem to be impossible. It is probably true that human beings, if they are destined to experience it at all, are gradually initiated into it by the affections of childhood. Love of parents towards their children—the genuine thing, as distinct from animal identification, is rarer than is commonly supposed—or the security of affection between children themselves powerfully predispose us towards the experience of love. At their best these experiences give a security and freedom, a foretaste of complete trust, which is ineradicable from the memory, and serves as an instinctive criterion by which we judge our adult human relations.

Whether by intuition, or because he was faithful to his own experience, Constant allows Adolphe none of these childish intimations of love. His mother is not mentioned, and we are to presume that, like Constant's own mother, she died at his birth. His relations with his father are cold and constrained. Constant lays great emphasis on these at the beginning of the story, and makes plain his conviction that the lack of contact and confidence between Adolphe and his father was the prime cause of his diffident and solitary character: of " his great impatience of the connections which surrounded him, and *his invin-*

*cible terror* of forming new ones." In the texture of the narrative the phrase is a strong one. Again, the simple phrase in the description of Adolphe's childish memories in Chapter VII is eloquent: "The elderly relatives who were the first to show signs of interest in me." It speaks of a childhood starved of affection, and a child to whom the condition of trust and security in love was unknown. In consequence, to the young man the condition was, in a sense, inconceivable. Its simplest elements were outside his experience.

To explain is not to exonerate. But the absence of a touchstone for his feelings increased enormously Adolphe's difficulty in breaking the bonds of the egotism into which his childish isolation had thrust him. There was plenty of nobility in his nature: indeed, were it not for that, we should not feel the sympathy for him that we do. Much of the power of the story comes from the fact that though we cannot love him as we love Ellenore, we find no mystery in the fact that she loved him. We feel she is not mistaken when at the end she says so simply and so movingly: "You are good." With less goodness, he would have made her suffer less; with less goodness, he would much more easily have found the strength to break with her entirely: not because he would in fact have been a stronger character, but because his generous impulses would have been weaker, and his selfishness would have had far less difficulty in overcoming them. It would have trampled them underfoot in its stride.

It is less than the truth to say baldly, as I said in the last chapter, that Adolphe is frightened by the anticipation of his own pain at Ellenore's pain and that, if he could have had the fortitude to endure it, Ellenore's wound would have been healed. It would indeed have been better if Adolphe could have endured in solitude the pain of her pain, because that would have been a crucial experience for him, from which he would have emerged a renewed and reintegrated man, capable of love. It is not because Adolphe was weaker than more brutal or callous natures would have been that he is to be condemned or pitied. Their strength and his weakness are not commensurable; they belong to different moral orders. Their strength is evil; his weakness is the impossibility of exercising that evil strength. He may plan it, but he cannot act it: because his moral instinct repudiates his thoughts as false. The courage he needed was the courage to wait and endure until the turmoil of his own being had subsided and clarified, and the conflict between false thoughts and a confused instinct had been resolved. The courage he needed was the courage not to violate but to resist his own emotion, and to have reverence enough for Ellenore's love of him not to return to her until he could return an undivided man. It is conceivable (I suppose) that he might never have been able to do this. In that case he would have had to bear his cross alone. But Ellenore would have known that the motive of his suffering was love, and her heart would have been at peace. But it is far more probable that, if Adolphe had the strength to wait and endure, and not to inflict upon her the torture of his own divided being, the inward division would have been healed.

The conflict between false thought and confused emotion characterises Adolphe from the beginning in his relation with Ellenore. False thought demands a conquest; confused emotion responds to her rare womanly excellence. Constant's description of the condition is masterly. He returns to the division again and again, and shows it unchanged but changing with the growth of the liaison. " My intention was to make a complete review of her character and mind as a cool and impartial observer; but every word she spoke to me seemed clothed in an inexplicable grace." Again, " Any one reading my heart, while I was away from her, would have taken me for a cold and unfeeling seducer; any one seeing me at her side would have seen in me a novice lover, tongue-tied and passionate. Both judgments would have been equally mistaken; there is no entire unity in man, and he is hardly ever completely sincere or completely false." In a little

142

while, after Ellenore has fled and returned, it
seems to Adolphe as though true feeling has
triumphed over false thought. " There were
no more calculations and plans; with the best
faith in the world I felt myself truly in love. It
was no longer the hope of conquest which impelled me; I was dominated by one thing alone
—the craving to see the woman I loved and to
enjoy her presence."

At this point false thought and confused
emotion are hopelessly embroiled with each
other; or we may say they have combined to
engender a false sentiment, which appears to
be like love but is not. If we are charitable
towards Adolphe, we shall say he has no
criterion by which to judge it. It is utterly
novel to him. Why should it not be love? He
has no longer the power to disentangle from
this strange emotion the workings of his egotism. But what Adolphe mistakes for love in
himself is his emotional response to the birth
and growth of true love towards him in
Ellenore. It is from the love which has begun
to suffuse her soul and body that the enchantment emanates for which he now craves. It
does not vastly matter how or why this love
of hers began. In fact, it began, or became
a possibility, when she received the letter containing his first declaration.

My long struggle with my own character, my
impatience at not being able to overcome it, my
uncertainty about the success of my attempt, lent

my letter an agitation which was very like love.
Besides I was fired by my own writing and, as I
finished the letter, I felt a touch of the passion
I had tried to express as forcibly as I could.

Adolphe was half deceived by it; Ellenore
wholly. But the quality of love depends not
on the object or exciting cause, but on the
quality of the soul in which it is conceived. Not
that one can imagine Ellenore loving a man
wholly bad or despicable. Adolphe was far
enough from that to make it entirely credible
and natural that he awakened love in her.
Once it was awakened in a woman so single-
hearted, it possessed her wholly: and she radi-
ated the enchantment of a mature woman who
for the first time is surrendered to love.

His craving for this radiance Adolphe mistakes for love. Indeed for a little while he is
content to live in it. But the serpent of false
thought soon rears its head again.

> But this calm was brief. Ellenore was the
> more on guard against her weakness because she
> was haunted by the memory of her lapses. My
> imagination, my desires, and a theory of manliness
> which I myself was unconscious of holding, re-
> volted against such a love. Always shy, often
> irritated, I complained, I lost control, I heaped
> reproaches on Ellenore. More than once she
> planned to break off a relation which only dis-
> quieted and troubled her life; as often I pacified
> her by my supplications, my disavowals and my
> tears.

An operative phrase in this passage almost
defies translation. In the French it is: " une

théorie de fatuité dont je ne m'apercevais pas moi-même." This is closely connected with a passage in the Preface to the Second Edition (1816). " Une doctrine de fatuité, tradition funeste, que lègue à la vanité de la génération qui s'élève la corruption de la génération qui a vieilli . . . semble les armer contre les larmes qui ne coulent pas encore." It is clear that the phrase in *Adolphe* really means " a theoretical notion of what constitutes foolishness," in the sense of naivety, or " innocence," or " being a mug "—the opposite of " a knowing one " or " a man of the world." So I have rendered it by what superficially appears to be its opposite: a theoretical notion of manliness (or man-of-the-worldliness). To be in love without having achieved physical possession of one's mistress is to be an " innocent," according to this doctrine. Adolphe does not hold it in full consciousness, says Constant: which I take to be an indication that his new emotional experience had wrought a change in him. The egotism is less conscious than it was. But in itself the attitude is the same as Adolphe's original desire for a conquest. It emerges in a slightly different emotional context after a brief period of happiness and calm in the radiance of Ellenore's love. Adolphe's psychological pattern is the same as it was before he wrote her the letter. He cannot enjoy what he has, because of his avidity to get more. Constant has previously described the condition.

**145**

My purpose of attracting her (Adolphe had said) put a new interest in my life and gave an unprecedented animation to my existence. This almost magical effect I attributed to her charm; I should have enjoyed it even more completely but for my engagement to my self-esteem. This self-esteem made a third between Ellenoré and me. I felt myself obliged to reach my goal as quickly as possible; and so I did not give myself up unreservedly to my feelings.

It is just the same with him when Ellenore has confessed her love. The only difference is that he is less conscious than he was before of his engagement to his self-esteem. But his egotism is there as before, a diabolical third between Ellenore and himself, in the guise of *amour propre*, urging him on impatiently to complete his conquest, preventing him from enjoying what he had, above all, disabling him from letting their love grow naturally.

Love between a man and a woman culminates naturally in physical union. That is its appointed end, and at the same time its new beginning. But since a man's desire is naturally more turbulent than a woman's, it is his duty and delight (if he is a true lover) to wait until the woman unfolds. The idea that governs love, if love can be said to be governed by an idea, is that of willing mutual surrender. The idea of conquest is alien and fatal to it. Adolphe was not wholly insusceptible to the idea of mutual surrender; he was not a man dominated by brute desire. The periods of calm and happiness he enjoyed in the radiance of Ellenore's love were periods of mutual surrender, appropriate to the phase of the growth of ripening love. But these periods of calm and mutual enjoyment were never suffered to develop themselves naturally and reach their own maturity. Always and inevitably, Adolphe's *amour propre* rises to interrupt the contact of their souls. It corrupts the potentiality of love in him. One might almost say it is also corrupted by it. At any rate it suffers an adulteration by emotion which makes it more insidious. Shyness and the desire for self-assertion in conquest combine to make Adolphe feel that Ellenore's delay in becoming his lover is a cruelty with which he is justified in reproaching her. This is a time-worn gambit of the calculating seducer, who knows what he is about. But the confusion between calculation and emotion in Adolphe is now such that it is easy for him to deceive himself. So he swings violently between outbursts of reproachful indignation and rapt submission. No wonder Ellenore thought of breaking off the relation. But by now she was too deeply in love, and Adolphe's distress was too real, or too plausible, for her not to believe that it was in the power of her love to make him happy. She surrenders.

Adolphe is not a mere conqueror. He does not behave or feel like one. Part of him responds, as it always does, to the radiance of Ellenore's love. Now that it is at last uttered

147

in and through her bodily tenderness, he too feels tenderness. For a little while indeed he is overcome by it. Constant's description of Adolphe's experience is remarkable, and ambiguous.

> Woe to the man who, in the first moments of a love-liaison, does not believe that it must be eternal! Woe to the man who, in the arms of the mistress he has won, retains a deadly prescience and foresees that he will be able to part from them! A woman whom her heart leads to surrender, has in that moment something touching and sacred. It is not pleasure, not nature, not the senses which corrupt; but the calculations which society makes habitual, and the reflections born of experience. I loved, I revered Ellenore infinitely more after she had given herself. I walked with pride among men; I looked upon them triumphantly. The air I breathed was in itself a delight. I rushed to Nature to thank her for the unhoped for and immeasurable blessing she had deigned to bestow on me.

It is ambiguous, because it does not plainly tell us whether Adolphe was or was not afflicted with the deadly prescience, did or did not believe that his love must be eternal. This vagueness is deliberate. The passage is a Delphic oracle which we may read as we will. Either we may believe that Adolphe has his moment of sincere illusion, and to that extent is innocent; or in the light of the sequel we may regard him as one who, already cursed with the deadly prescience, deservedly suffers the woe that is foretold. And this is really the more probable and convincing. But the

studied ambiguity of the whole passage is
masterly. The self-revelation of Adolphe in
the mixture of tenderness and egotism is completely plausible. The combination of the
sense of " something touching and sacred " in
the surrendered Ellenore with " the look of
triumph " over the surrender; the comfortable
transfer to society of the blame for the deadly
prescience it teaches—as though it were not in
his power to refuse the instruction; the profound self-deception of " I loved, I revered
Ellenore infinitely more after she had given
herself "—it is an extraordinary *tour de force*;
or so it would be if Adolphe were entirely a
creature of the imagination. And it remains
something of the kind even when we know that
much of the psychological substance of
Adolphe is autobiographical. As Rousseau
said of a greater matter, " Ce n'est pas ainsi
qu'on invente "; but it needed a great deal of
art, and a remarkable detachment, to tell the
truth so well.

By now we have learned to distrust the
word " love " when it comes from Adolphe's
pen. We are driven to ask what he means
when he says " he loved her infinitely more
after she had given herself." It seems fairly
plain that, though there is an increase in the
intensity of emotion, it is not an increase of
love at all. What Adolphe loves, the object
for which he feels the more intense emotion is
not Ellenore, in her own unique identity, so

much as Ellenore, the conquered woman. It is
not Ellenore, in herself, who is touching and
sacred, but the Ellenore who is the victim and
who has surrendered herself in vain: Ellenore
seen as a woman whom the imaginary compul-
sions of society, or the reasonings of worldly
wisdom, will "compel" him to abandon: the
Ellenore who is defined, circumscribed and de-
natured by his own " deadly prescience," which
is a prescience not of anything in the future
which by the nature of things must be, but
of something for which he himself will be
wholly responsible. In other words, the
emotion which overwhelms him, and which he
calls an infinitely greater love than he had felt
before, is not love at all, but a form of the
totally different emotion of pity. And since it
is pity for the victim of his own egotism and
weakness, it is a very different emotion, and
a much more equivocal one, than pity for the
victim of a misfortune in which the pitier has
had no hand. In that case pity is the only
possible, the only appropriate emotion, and if
it is genuine it proves itself by rendering
succour, if succour can be given. But this
pity of Adolphe's is really spurious. If it were
genuine it would render succour. Succour is
simple to give. All it requires is the decision
not to abandon Ellenore, by turning a deaf ear
to the calculations which society makes
habitual and shutting the door on the
reflexions of so-called experience. By that

simple means this spurious pity would abolish the cause of its own existence. It is, therefore, what Dostoevsky would call " a monkey-cari-cature" of the genuine emotion. It is the false emotion which apes the part of the genuine one in the nature of a sentimental egotist. Subjectively, it is no doubt a power-ful emotion, and arouses much intensity of feeling; but since it is by inward necessity pre-cluded from finding expression in an integral and redemptive act, which would remove it entirely, it feeds upon and proliferates itself.

From this point onwards the story of Adolphe is the story of this spurious pity battening upon its own victim. It is important to have the elements of the situation clear. What poisons the relation of Adolphe and Ellenore is Adolphe's persuasion that it is to be a transient "affair." At the beginning he in-tends it to be transient. That is the self-imposed condition on which he seeks it. The idea that he might, unwittingly, enter a rela-tion which by its own nature repels the notion of transience does not enter his head. It is not a possibility within the scheme of things; it is a condition which he cannot conceive: for love which is in virtue of its own nature bind-ing involves a destruction of the ego which he cannot imagine, and if he could, he would regard as intolerable. For him it would be an annihilation of himself, an invitation into nothingness. But the moment comes when he is exposed to the power of the love he has awakened in Ellenore. It is almost overwhelming. In order to save himself intact he clings to the idea that the relation must be transient; and to answer his need of self-preservation this idea is subtly transformed. His superficial philosophy comes to his aid. It is no longer he who desires and wills that it shall be transient: it is a necessity which derives from a law of nature. Death is the end of all. Since death sets a term to the loyallest love, it is the part of wisdom for all love to anticipate its own death. Love is manifestly ephemeral; it is the merest honesty for it to digest the knowledge of its own ephemerality, and to accept the fact that every love-relation is condemned by the nature of things to be only an episode.

This superficial philosophy is as much the expression of Adolphe's egotism as was the intention that his affair with Ellenore should be merely an affair. It is invoked to conceal from himself the fact that his desire that his relation with her shall be transient is his own decision. It would be invalidated by the experience of love. The tragedy is that through the armour of this false philosophy love can gain no entrance. Love must either destroy it, or be destroyed by it: for it makes love trivial, by reducing it to the status of a biological episode.

In saying that Adolphe's attitude and

philosophy is false, we are taking an engagement and declaring a faith. In the terms of
the story, we are declaring that the right and
the truth is with Ellenore. This cannot be
proved. But the power of Constant's story
lies in the fact that it is revealed. It was not
any fidelity to autobiographical experience, but
an unerring imagination which made Constant
represent Ellenore as an essentially religious
soul. At this level the story is one of a struggle
between religion and scepticism, in which
scepticism wins a deadly victory. Ellenore is
killed by it, and Adolphe ruined. Nevertheless,
Ellenore's fidelity to love leaves us with a sense
of spiritual triumph. In this sense, *Adolphe*
is a true tragedy, and a very remarkable one.

# CHAPTER III

The chief positive influence on the development of Adolphe's character, according to the story, was an older woman. Adolphe has stressed the lack of any tender intimacy in boyhood between himself and his father. His mother, we have assumed, died like Constant's own, in childbirth. The more potent, accordingly, was the effect upon him of a tenderly intimate relation with an older woman. Significantly, the description of her is introduced to explain why the idea of death had such dominion over his mind.

This indifference to everything was strengthened by the idea of death—an idea which had impressed me at a very early age, and men's insensitiveness to which has always been incomprehensible to me. When I was seventeen, I witnessed the death of an older woman, whose distinguished and unusual mind had begun to develop my own. She, like many others, at the beginning of her career, had entered society, with which she was unfamiliar, with the consciousness of a great force of soul and truly powerful faculties; also, like many others, because she did not submit to its artificial but necessary conventions, she had seen her hopes deceived, and her youth pass without happiness. Old age overtook her at last but could not subdue her. She lived in a château near one of our estates, retired and discontented; her mind was her only resource, and with her mind she analysed everything. For nearly a year, in our unending conversations, we reviewed life in all its aspects, with death always at the end of all. After talking of death so much with her, I saw death strike her before my eyes.

It is generally agreed that the original of this woman is Madame de Charrière, a neighbour and confidant of Constant's youth in Switzerland. She was not quite so much older than young Constant as she appears in the story—twenty-eight years to be exact. A good deal of Constant's correspondence with Madame de Charrière is extant, and it shows plainly that she did much, as Adolphe says, to develop his mind, and that he found in her the first real confidant of his retiring nature. Although in what I have read of the correspondence there is no direct evidence of their having talked much of death, it is clear enough that the accepted background of their intellectual and sentimental relation was a common conviction that "Death is the end of all." Madame de Charrière was a woman whose mind had been definitely formed by the scepticism of the eighteenth century; Constant was a young man whose pessimism was not yet in grain. It partly depended on the mature woman's influence whether the bias of his mind would be confirmed or corrected. It was confirmed. She encouraged his melancholy, by attaching to it the tenderness and charm of an intimate confidence. A letter he wrote to her after spending two months with her gives us a glimpse of the process at work. He was twenty-four years old.

> It is exactly a fortnight, Madame, that at this very hour, at ten minutes past ten, we were

sitting by the fire in the kitchen; Rose was behind
us, and got up from time to time to put little bits
of wood on the fire, which she broke up as they
were needed; and we talked on the theme: great
wits to madness are allied. We were happy: I was
anyhow. There is a kind of pleasure in anticipating the moment of a painful separation. This idea,
cruel though it is, makes every instant precious:
every one we enjoy is so much snatched from
destiny; and we experience a kind of vibration, a
physical and moral thrill, which it would be
equally false to call a pleasure without pain, or a
pain without pleasure. I don't know if I am
talking nonsense; you must judge, but I think I
know what I mean.

Constant did not see Madame de Charrière
die; nor was he seventeen when she did die.
She died, in fact, in 1805, when Constant
was forty. Their intimate intellectual and
emotional friendship lasted until Constant was
thirty, and Madame de Staël took possession
of him. It faded then into a grateful affection
on his side and a tender disappointment on
hers. The charming little sketch of her in
*Adolphe* is in part a pious tribute to her
memory.

The character of Adolphe may be taken
in substance as a portrait of the youthful
Constant, though I should prefer to call it an
imaginative projection by Constant of an
earlier aspect of himself into circumstances
such as he had never experienced: a love for a
woman such as he had never met.

Confirmed, as we may suppose, in his
youthful bent towards pessimism by the

scepticism and sentiment of Madame de Charrière, yet belonging to a younger generation touched by the romantic afflatus, the young Constant, portrayed in Adolphe, was a peculiar prey to the conflict between Christian sensibility and unbelief. The mystery of death fascinated him; he could not take death for granted. Adolphe is astonished by the indifference of men towards it, and the sombre power of the scene of Ellenore's death is an incontrovertible testimony to the seriousness of his concern, and the reality of his awe. Death overshadows life and love, and in the shade of its wing both are chilled. The belief in the finality of death deals death. It kills love at its birth in Adolphe and so kills Ellenore, whose life now depends on love.

As was inevitable, Constant mingles the naive and slightly theatrical pessimism of youth with the much more serious pessimism of a mature man. To disentangle entirely the elements of youthful cynicism in the character of Adolphe from the profounder philosophy in which the story was conceived is difficult, if not perhaps impossible. But, although *Adolphe* is a book about a young man, it is very far from being a young man's book. Adolphe's psychology is, I think, fundamentally true; but he is even more a symbol than a character. His presentiment of the transience of love disturbs him more than he knows or expresses; in the last analysis the motive that impels him is less

something that we can fairly call egotism than
a kind of fatality.   It is as though he were the
unconscious and perhaps unwilling bearer of
a seed of death; and this seed of death derives
from a deeper contemplation of death than any
attributed to the young Adolphe in the book
itself.   It is merely hinted at in the influence
which the spectacle of the older woman's
death is said to have had on Adolphe.   This
contemplation of death belongs to the soul of
the mature Constant.   We may fairly describe it as the contemplation of a pre-Christian
idea of death by a Christian sensibility.   The
reverberation is terribly disturbing; for by
passing through a Christian sensibility, the
pre-Christian idea of death acquires as it were
a supernatural power.   It can no longer be
accepted, as death was accepted by the pre-
Christian soul; it becomes a dynamic power
of devastation, laying waste the springs of life.

It must be so, for the Christian sensibility
has grown from the faith that love is the
supreme power in the universe, everlasting and
indestructible.   Just as the final parable of
Jesus teaches that in the day of Judgment, the
smallest act of love, even though unconsidered
and forgotten, will be rewarded by eternal life,
so for the Christian sensibility the disinterested
devotion of love has an absolute validity.   It
cannot be wasted or destroyed.   And this
valuation of love persists and is ineradicable,
even when the belief in the after-life has

decayed.  But now there is an impasse.  Death,
now envisaged as annihilation, menaces love
with absolute waste.  But love cannot be discarded because the intellect declares it to be
transient and vain.  It is not discarded; but,
so long as the intellect holds to its position, it
is chilled and corrupted.  The only way out of
this impasse is to surrender completely to the
experience of love, and so permit it to become
itself the evidence of its own transcendency.
Love is then known to be a new dimension of
experience, valid and supreme in its own right,
which is able by its own sovereign power to
set at nought the false pretentions of the intellect.  It is no longer death which reveals
the transience of love.  Love reveals the
transience of death.

This experience and the conviction it
creates may lead to a deeper understanding
and a new acceptance of the Christian faith
itself.  For the Christian faith, in its origin and
essence, appears to be nothing other than the
declaration that love *is* self-validating, and
veritably a new dimension of experience, in
which alone the meaning of life is revealed.
That is the abiding content of Jesus's primary
assertion that God is a loving Father; it is
equally the abiding content of the distinctive
Christian revelation that in the death of Jesus,
obedient unto death to love, the meaning of
life and the nature of God is manifest.  The love
with which the receptive soul responds to that

manifestation of love carries it into the new dimension of experience: and the apparatus of Christian dogma, with all its majesty and subtlety, appears to be nothing but the effort of the human mind to declare what it is that is revealed. The effort is unavoidable; it will never cease to be made, even when men know it seeks to utter the unutterable. As Wittgenstein says, " What can be revealed cannot be uttered."

So it is with Constant's story. It is the story of the struggle between a Christian sensibility in which the power of love has been debilitated and corrupted by the sinister power of an intellectual idea of death, and a Christian sensibility which has not been contaminated and for which the power of love has all its pristine virtue of revelation and renewal. Through Adolphe the power of death works its will; but it destroys only what it can destroy. It destroys Ellenore's body; her bodily strength is wasted in the effort to make Adolphe penetrable to love. But the power of death cannot destroy her soul, redeemed and fortified by love. This is the impression produced by the story, although the author is ruthless in his emphasis on the comprehensive destruction wrought by the approach of death.

> I watched her move forward step by step to destruction. I saw the signs of coming death engrave themselves on her noble and expressive face. It was lamentable and humiliating to see her proud and fiery character confusedly and in-

coherently impressed by bodily suffering, as
though in these terrible moments, the soul, galled
by the body, was being totally changed to accommodate itself less painfully to the organic
degradation.

The implication is deliberate. As the body
disintegrates, so does the soul. Adolphe certainly believed that; whether Constant himself
did, we shall consider later. Perhaps he did
not know himself. Perhaps it was simply the
urge to veracity which made him spare himself and us nothing of the spectacle of
Ellenore's bodily dissolution. All the more
remarkable and impressive is the conviction
which abides with us that in Ellenore love is
triumphant. And this in spite not only of her
death, but—perhaps even more important—of
her own doubt of love's power. " I have many
sins to expiate. Perhaps my love for you was
a sin. But I should not believe it, if my love
could have made you happy."

I have remarked on these pathetic and
significant words before. They reveal the last
infirmity of a noble mind—a woman's noble
mind. For it is no touchstone of the purity or
the efficacy of love, that it should have the
power to make the beloved happy. That
depends upon him. Love is a grace to which,
on peril of our souls, we must respond; and to
respond is to surrender. There is no safe and
prudent midway point where we can adjust our
service as between God and Mammon.
Adolphe's effort to find one only increased his

weakness and Ellenore's suffering. Adolphe, being what he was, could not respond. The fault was not in her but in him. But it is in the nature of a loving woman to believe that love in her has power, of itself, to make her beloved happy. Therefore, if it fails to do so, it lacks its own proper virtue, and her love is at fault. For a moment Ellenore half-believed —or the thought passes across her mind—that her love had been insufficient; perhaps also that its virtue was defective because it was, by the standard of conventional morality, a " sinful " love.

Whether Ellenore in her dying confession expiated it as a sin, there is no knowing. I imagine she made her peace with God without difficulty, on her own terms: that is to say, on her own terms as compared with the official conditions of absolution, but on God's own terms as far as He was concerned. She had no need of mediators; she had obeyed Him faithfully, and had not confused God's ordinance with the commands of men or the conventions of society. She had obeyed love. To the extent that she had felt love, she had given complete fidelity: to the greater love, a new and greater fidelity. The doubt that had passed through her mind was only a temptation: a very subtle temptation—to believe that the power of love can work in another dimension than that of love itself, and that it has failed, or is wrong, because it cannot.

162

Whether Constant consciously intended to convey all this, I do not presume to say. But that his story does convey it is certain. Ellenore's love, in spite of her doubt and her death, is triumphant. In virtue of its power to make this enduring impression, *Adolphe* is a true tragedy. And Constant's intuitive sense of values is unerring when he makes Ellenore a deeply Christian woman, at one and the same time religious in the conventional sense—a faithfully practising Christian—and loyal to her own courageous and original conviction of the true relation of Christian piety and human love. At one level indeed Constant strains outward probability to make this plain. We may well ask ourselves, on reflection, why Ellenore remains, for the ten years before her meeting with Adolphe, merely the mistress of Count P———. He is not married; he has acknowledged her children as the heirs to his fortune; and even when Ellenore has left him he is generous enough to offer to bestow half his wealth upon her. She is his equal in birth. Why then do they not marry? The only valid answer, I think, is that it is important, at a higher level than that of realistic probability, that Ellenore's loves should never be " legitimate," never sanctioned by society and moral convention. She is a pure case—the thing itself. In order to have full significance, she has to be a woman who deliberately chooses that her love-relations shall be sanctioned by

love alone.    It is arguable and possible that
Constant felt that if Ellenore had been married
to the Count her religious soul would have
been inhibited from responding to Adolphe.
But my strong impression is that the necessity
of Ellenore being unmarried belongs to a
different plane.    Just as she never desires to
be married to Adolphe (as he tells the Baron
in Ch. VII) so she never desired to be married
to the Count.    The fact that with the Count
she is sensitive about her equivocal situation
is entirely compatible with this; and the fact
that with Adolphe she ceases to be sensitive
about it is an indication of the new depth of
feeling that has been aroused in her.

The significance of Ellenore's deliberate
dissociation of love from marriage is something of which Constant himself is much more
aware than Adolphe.    Adolphe is merely
struck by what appear to him the contradictions in her character.

> She had a number of prejudices; but they
> were all opposed to her interest.  She set the
> highest value on regularity of conduct, precisely
> because her own was irregular by conventional
> standards.    She was very religious, because
> religion rigorously condemned her mode of life.
> In conversation she severely rejected what other
> women would have considered innocent
> pleasantries, because she was always afraid that
> her situation might be thought to justify
> pleasantries of another sort being addressed to
> her.    She would have liked to receive only men
> of the highest rank and the most exemplary morals,
> because the kind of women to whom she shuddered

to be compared ordinarily form a mixed society for themselves: they are resigned to their loss of consideration and look only for amusement in their social relations.

It is Adolphe's analysis, not Constant's. Constant himself, for all his love of paradox and his habit of saying that " a truth is complete only when it has been injected with its contrary," would certainly not have been guilty of the naivety of the second and third of these pronouncements. Nothing in the character of Ellenore as subsequently revealed gives any warrant to the statement that " she was religious *because* religion condemned her mode of life." She was naturally Christian, and she had the insight and the courage to believe that there was nothing contrary to Christianity in her mode of life. That it was outwardly equivocal concerned her only in so far as it gave occasion to ignoble minds to interpret her by their own standards. Again, she set the highest value on regularity of conduct, not *because* her own was irregular; but because levity of conduct was abhorrent to her. Since fidelity in love was her supreme value, she naturally shrank from being classed with women who regarded it as trivial.

Adolphe's analysis is superficial. To be fair to him one might say that his acquaintance with Ellenore was superficial, too, at the time when the analysis is supposed to be made; and indeed the impression made by the last chapter of the story is that Adolphe comes to realise how superficial his understanding of Ellenore has been. Logically his final understanding of Ellenore should have informed the whole of his narrative: but this sort of logic has no validity in a work of the imagination. And Constant did well to reject it. It is sufficient for us to realise that not one of Ellenore's " prejudices " (as Adolphe calls them) is justly so described, and the reasons he gives for some of them are childish.

But this view of Ellenore's character is one that encourages him to his attempt at conquest. Externally and uncomprehendingly, he sees her capacity for love; and he needs love, or thinks he does. Externally and uncomprehendingly, he sees her capacity for fidelity and her horror of a casual liaison; and that is a stimulus to his vanity, which craves an exceptional triumph. Here is a defence which no common philanderer can penetrate; here is " a conquest worthy of himself." He achieves it; in the process he deceives himself, and he deceives Ellenore. But he is caught in a fatal toil. He is a better man than his ego. He experiences emotions unknown to him, for which he is unprepared. What his conscious deception could never have achieved, these unfamiliar emotions achieve. It is they which persuade Ellenore, and attract to him the full radiance of her love. Now, when he seeks to extricate himself, he cannot. He cannot play his chosen part to the end. He is a hopelessly

166

divided man.  Two parts of him are resolute to make an end of the relation; a third part is powerless to inflict the suffering: or so it appears to him.  But, in fact, he has touched the fringe of a realm of experience, from which he dares not part.  He can find in himself the strength neither to enter fully into it nor to abandon it.  So he appears to batten on the suffering of Ellenore like a vampire.  He condemns her to death.  The separation he longs for, she has to make.  Since she cannot make it by any conscious and deliberate act; she makes it by dying; or rather it is made for her by death.  Then, by a grim irony, Adolphe comes his nearest to loving Ellenore.  In this irony is nothing forced.  It cuts deep, because it is true.  Adolphe can love her only when the approach of death makes separation certain.

# CHAPTER IV

We return to the story, which we have in part anticipated. Ellenore has surrendered herself to love, body and soul. In a very little while Adolphe begins to chafe under the bond. He takes it hardly that he is not free to come and go as he will. As usual, he puts the blame on the exigences of the social order. The sentence in which the serpent first raises his head is the last of these.

> She could hardly bear two hours' separation. She anxiously fixed the precise moment of my return. I joyfully agreed; I was grateful, I was happy at the feeling she showed for me. Nevertheless, the interests of common life cannot be arbitrarily fitted to all our desires.

Adolphe had no social duties; he had carefully avoided any contacts which might impose them. And social pleasures had no appeal for him. It is the old abstract freedom for its own sake after which he hankers. He confesses as much.

> With Ellenore I did not in the least regret these pleasures of social life, which never attracted me particularly, but I would have preferred to renounce them more spontaneously. It would have been more delightful to go back to her of my own free will, without saying to myself: " It is time, she is anxiously waiting for me "; without the idea of her distress being mixed with the happiness of seeing her again. Ellenore was surely an acute pleasure in my existence, but she was no longer a goal; she had become a tie.

It calls for no comment, except perhaps that it contains a peculiar self-deception. The happiness of seeing Ellenore again would not have been marred by the thought of her distress, if Adolphe had resolved not to distress her, by getting back in time. Had necessity detained him, she would have been quick to forgive. The idea of her distress is potent, only because he does not really want to be back in time, and that because he clutches at the false idea of freedom. It is not only the inordinate claims of love that he resents, but the just ones as well: and indeed these most of all.

Then, by a characteristic twist, he persuades himself that his craving for freedom is really for the sake of Ellenore. He is afraid of compromising her. His constant presence would create a scandal.

> I trembled at the idea of upsetting her existence. I felt that we could not be united for ever, and that it was my sacred duty to respect her security. I gave her counsels of prudence, while assuring her of my love.

Whenever Adolphe uses the word "sacred," we prick up our ears; it is the signal of a special refinement in self-deception. The source of this concern for Ellenore's reputation is manifest. It is Adolphe's determination that their love shall be only a passing intrigue. He puts it beautifully: he felt that they could not be united for ever; therefore it is his "sacred duty" not to disturb the even tenour of her life. What he means is that it is his " sacred duty " to prevent her from disturbing the even tenour of his own.

Instinctively, Ellenore senses that his real concern is not for her, but for himself. A cold wind touches the rose. Counsels of prudence are simply alien to her. She has given herself to love, and all her desire is to follow where love bids. She is now single, in heart and mind; she cannot play a part, and she cannot and does not conceal her disappointment. She needs a lot of reassuring, even though she longs to be reassured. And the effort to reassure her is painful to Adolphe.

" Nevertheless," he says superbly, " I was not unhappy. . . . . I felt I was doing her good." The picture of Adolphe in this chapter (IV) is masterly. Seldom has such a complex character been revealed in so few words.

> Besides, the dim idea that by the sheer nature of things this liaison could not last, saddening though it was in many ways, nevertheless served to quieten me in my fits of weariness or impatience . . . . All these considerations urged me to give and receive all the happiness I could. Certain of the years, I did not haggle over the days.

It sounds almost like generosity, and perhaps Adolphe felt it was. More probably he sought some such refinement of sensation as young Constant had experienced in the kitchen with Madame de Charrière. The relation between the two conditions is obvious.

> There is a kind of pleasure (he wrote to

170

Madame de Charrière) in anticipating the moment
of a painful separation. This idea, cruel though it
is, makes every instant precious: every one we enjoy is so much snatched from destiny; and we experience a kind of vibration, a physical and moral
thrill, which it would be equally false to call a
pleasure without pain, or a pain without pleasure.

There we have the outline, the pencil
sketch, of the psychological pattern of Adolphe.
But there it is fresh and innocent: the report
of a boyish explorer of the *pays du tendre*. No
doubt there was a sentimental attachment
between young Constant and Madame de
Charrière; but if there was more on her side
(as perhaps there was) it was her business to
keep it under control, for she was old enough
to be his mother. So the egotism of "We
were happy; I was anyhow" does not offend
us. It is frank and natural; and if it hurt
Madame a little, it probably did her good.

But in the relation between Adolphe and
Ellenore this same pattern becomes menacing
and deadly. The insensitiveness of Adolphe's
"I was not unhappy.... I felt that I was doing
her good" is now intolerable. The egotism of
the adolescent is natural and healthy; the
egotism of the adult man is unnatural and
diseased. The superficial philosophy of transience has been used to justify egotism in
seeking to inspire love, and now it is used to
reconcile the soul to the practice of a deception
as shocking as it is vain. It stands in the
order of things, says Adolphe, that my tie

shall be broken. I have only to let the sum of things have its way and I shall be free. Destiny—that idol of the selfish heart—thus absolves me from all engagement, all commitment. It now sets me free to extract all the pleasure I can from the love it made me free to inspire. Since Ellenore's unhappiness makes me unhappy, and thus deprives me of pleasure, I am free to remove her unhappiness in any way I can—short, of course, of sacrificing an atom of the freedom which the order of things has bestowed on me. Unfortunately, to remove the cause of Ellenore's unhappiness requires me to give her that conviction of security in my love which alone can make her happy. This I am forbidden to give by the order of things which has decreed that there can be no security in love. Thus it also permits that, in order that I may not be made unhappy by her unhappiness, I may try to deceive her to the utmost of my power. She, alas, will not be really deceived by my assurances that she can be secure in my love, any more than I shall be deceived myself. But we shall do our best. I, at any rate, want her to be deceived—I am most anxious to do her good; and she may perhaps prefer to deceive herself rather than face the emptiness of my professions. Let us gather our roses while we may, and ignore the envious and obvious worm.

But Ellenore does not deceive herself. The Count returns and suspects. Ellenore herself cares nothing if he does. But Adolphe is terrified at the threatened collapse of his plans. His counsels of prudence became impassioned. Ellenore reads her doom.

> She listened to me in silence for a long while; she was deathly pale. "One way or another (she said at last) you will be going soon. Don't let us anticipate the moment. Don't worry about me. Let us gain days, gain hours. Days—hours—that is all I need. Adolphe, I have a presentiment that I shall die in your arms."

At the first reading the full depth of the vibration may escape us. We may, at first, even think it is one more romantic woman threatening suicide. But it is the voice of doom. In a moment of vision Ellenore sees her lover as he is—not as he thinks he is, not as she wants to believe he is—but as he *is*; the messenger and vehicle of death to love. And since she is now all love, she sees him as the messenger and vehicle of death to her.

She does not love him less, because she knows he will be fatal to her. She does not say, as it seems she might, and as others will, that a malevolent destiny has inspired her with love for an unworthy man. An unworthy man could not be the messenger of death to Ellenore. She recognises that there is that in him which could inspire love in her—a total love such as she had never felt before: a love for which she is, and remains to the end, grateful. It is no mean destiny to be chosen the daughter of God. And Adolphe has been the instrument of her destiny, the means of her salvation.

What is it in Adolphe that has inspired and will retain her love? At one level, his very weakness—the real misery of the divided being, whose heart can never be at peace with his mind, whose intellect poisons and corrupts his feelings but cannot destroy them. For a little while Ellenore had believed that she, and she alone, could save him and bring him happiness: to do it she had surrendered herself completely to love. That dazzling promise had set almost as soon as it had risen. That is the Adolphe who had awakened love in her; but the Adolphe who retains her love and will retain it to the end is not quite the same. It is the Adolphe whose inward division love has failed to heal —love which she knows to be flawless and entire. It has brought him only one strange emotion which his mind has corrupted—one terrifying onslaught upon his freedom. The only power that could heal this disease, not having healed it, has made it incurable. The Adolphe whom Ellenore sees as he is in her moment of vision, more surely than she, is also doomed.

She is only doomed to die; her love will remain, intact and indestructible. He is doomed to love, incapable of love, capable of knowing only that the angel troubled the waters of the pool while he was rooted immobile to the side, as in a horrible dream; capable of loving Ellenore only when love can be no more than an unappeasable regret, capable of loving Ellenore only when she is dying, and because she is dead. *Tendebatque manus ripae ulterioris amore.*\*

But Ellenore's presentiment is not only that she will die, but that she will die in Adolphe's arms. Is that more than a purely artistic completion—rounding off the pattern to heighten the emotional appeal of the story to the extreme? Surely it is. It follows from the nature of Adolphe's inward division that he will never wholly resist the appeal of Ellenore's suffering. He cannot change himself, or suffer himself to be changed, so as to remove the cause of her suffering. On the contrary, the more she suffers by his acts and attitude, the more powerful is the attraction she exerts upon him; the more powerfully her suffering attracts him, the more rebellious is he against the compulsion, and the more, by his words and attitude, he increases her suffering. He is doomed to go on standing by to give yet another turn to the rack on which Ellenore is stretched.

The terrible logic of their relation seems to me without a flaw. An Adolphe who could resist Ellenore's suffering would be an Adolphe

---

\* " And stretched out his hands in vain longing for the further shore." Aeneid VI, 314.

who could not have inspired love in Ellenore. To a calculating and heartless seducer, however subtle, she would never have given her heart. It is to the element of true feeling in her lover, however mingled with base metal, that she has responded. On the other hand, although I can conceive an Adolphe who might find in himself the strength honestly to confess to her the nature of the deadly division within him, and to convince her of the necessity of a separation while he went apart and wrestled with his demon alone, I have to confess that this is another Adolphe: a man capable of at least the beginnings of radical self-change. He might be a plausible character: the change would do no psychological violence to his known elements. But *Adolphe* would then be quite another story, and certainly not an equally impressive one.

There is, of course, always the possibility of confusion when we regard, as we must, the characters of a work of fiction as really existing: and the possibility of confusion is greatest when the work is of an order so high that the happenings seem inevitable, and we speak naturally of a doom or destiny at work. It is easy to forget that, after all, it is the author who has doomed them. It was Benjamin Constant who placed Ellenore and Adolphe under a doom. He might have saved them; and if he had been a Dickens he would have done, at no matter what cost to psychological probability.    But a Dickens could never have conceived these two particular characters at all.   They have a spiritual veracity of a kind that Dickens neither attempted or desired. Part of the extraordinary power of *Adolphe* comes from our feeling that Constant has reduced the element of arbitrariness in his story to an absolute minimum.    Given the meeting of these two people, what happened to them is what must have happened to them. To conceive Adolphe with just so much more strength of character to have been able to be, at a given moment, completely honest with Ellenore, as I have just conceived him, though it involves no violent improbability, imposes just sufficient strain upon our expectation to make us conscious of the astonishing justice of Constant's delineation.

Nevertheless, to say, as I have said, that the logic of the relation between Adolphe and Ellenore is flawless, is a metaphor.    It is indeed a metaphor when applied to any human relation: though whether we believe that depends on whether we hold, as an article of faith, that human beings are always capable of radical change.    I do.    But the act required to open the possibility of change may be vastly difficult.    A religious conversion is demanded. And what we are really imagining when we imagine Adolphe finding the strength to be honest with Ellenore is that this process of conversion has begun.    Such a process is outside the scope of Constant's story. It would be interesting to know whether Constant believed it possible. My feeling is that Constant doomed Adolphe because he *could* not do otherwise: by which I mean that he could not have represented Adolphe undergoing the " conversion " with a fidelity and convincingness comparable to that with which he has represented Adolphe impenetrable to grace. The unchanging and unchanged Adolphe he knew : he looked into his own youthful heart and wrote. The other would have been a conjecture, or an anachronism.

However that may be—and we shall return to it—the Adolphe whom Ellenore sees in her moment of vision is the Adolphe who cannot change. This is Adolphe as he is— the man whose heart has been verily poisoned by the false philosophy of his mind. She knows that he will kill her. The deadly blow has indeed already been struck. In this instant of prescience she knows that death is quite near. And it is against the background of that foreknowledge that she cries : " Let us gain days, gain hours. Days—hours—that is all I need." Of course, Adolphe does not understand her meaning. To him, she is merely pleading that he shall not leave her yet ; and her presentiment is only the threat of an overwrought and apprehensive woman. That she is pleading with him to stay with her until she dies, plead-

ing with him that this is possible even for him
because her death will not be long delayed,
does not enter his head. The tragic irony is
humanly heart-rending, and artistically magnificent.

The tragic irony is the more impressive,
because we feel that Ellenore herself does not
quite know what she means. She has had an
instant of inspired foreknowledge; a vision
that she is in the grip of destiny. But the
moment passes, the knowledge is hidden again.
She becomes simply a loving and passionate
woman, haunted by an inward and unspoken
fear. When, a little later, the letter comes from
Adolphe's father bidding him return, Ellenore
speaks with a different voice.

> "Adolphe, you see I cannot live without you;
> I do not know what will happen to my future, but
> I beseech you, do not go yet. Find excuses for
> staying. Ask your father for six months longer.
> Six months—is that so long?"

The change is subtle, of angle rather than
substance, as though Ellenore saw the same
adamantine truth from another side, and at a
greater distance. "Let me not die without
you" is changed to "I cannot live without
you; I do not know what will happen to my
future." Or it is as though a veil of love and
tears was drawn across her previous vision,
hiding the certainty of death. She turns back,
like a true woman, to live in the present, and
thrusts away the future. From known it
becomes unknown again. It is like the blood

179

creeping back into her pale face. Now she will live so long as Adolphe remains with her—only so long, indeed. But there is a difference between this and " Stay just long enough for me to die."

Again the tragic irony is intense. When Ellenore has dropped a veil over the future, her words: " I cannot live without you " appear to be simple. Without Adolphe's physical presence she cannot live. But that does not alter the fact that the future has been prophetically seen. In his presence she will die. The separation which will kill her is not physical at all: it is the separation of their souls. That is irremediable, except by a miracle of grace to Adolphe. The separation of their souls is, at best, only concealed by their bodily co-presence: in reality, indeed, it is increased and sharpened by it. Their being together is a kind of dreadful drug which infects their life with a consuming intensity: so that the very word " life " becomes equivocal. " I cannot live without you " and " I shall die with you " are really the same. To live with him is such an intensity of emotion and suffering that her life must be consumed. At the same time " I cannot live without you " has its full meaning on the spiritual level. The separation of their souls will kill her. Her last words: " Six months—is that so long?" vibrate on both levels at once. Six months to live? Six months to die? There is yet a third meaning: the simplest of all, yet perhaps the most pathetic. "Six months more with me—to your impatience, does it seem an age?"

Her pathos now wrings Adolphe to the heart. This is the note to which he will respond. He has plucked it from her soul, as though it were an instrument he played on with deathly skill. He in turn vibrates to it, and transmits the vibration even to his father. "I wrote to him with the emotion I felt at her pain . . . . When I put my letter in the post, I ardently desired to obtain the consent I asked for." Since his father is by no means devoid of affection for him, he obtains his desire. But before he tells Ellenore, he has time to be appalled at the prospect of six months' more bondage. He tells her the news in a tone which wounds her to the quick, and at the same time stings her vanity, for there is much of the mere woman in her still. They fling cruel words at each other: which, though they are reconciled, they cannot forget. And the quarrels recur.

After our bitterest quarrels, she was just as eager to see me again, and fixed the time of our meetings just as carefully as though our union were full of peace and tenderness. I have often thought that my own behaviour helped to keep her in this disposition. If I had loved her as she loved me, she would have been calmer; she would herself have reflected on the dangers she defied. But all prudence was hateful to her, since the prudence came from me; she did not reckon her sacrifices,

since she was bent on making me accept them; she
had no time to grow colder towards me, because
all her time and strength were taken in holding
me.

In these reflections of Adolphe's there is
one true statement, and only one: " If I had
loved her as she loved me, she would have
been calmer." She would indeed: not only
calmer, but completely happy, which is more
important. Adolphe's one truth is a half-
truth, because it, like all the rest which are not
even half-truths, is based on a misunderstanding and belittlement of Ellenore's love. If he
had loved her as she loved him, she would not
have reflected on the dangers she defied—not
in his sense of reflecting on them, anyhow.
She would not have been more prudent, in his
meaning of prudence; she would not have
reckoned her sacrifices, which in that case
would not have seemed to her sacrifices at all.
She would have made them all, and the inconceivable Adolphe, who loved her as she loved
him, would have wanted her to make them.
She might have made them less precipitately;
but she certainly would have made them, and
made them gaily and radiantly, as though they
were the most natural thing in the world.

The truth is that the condition which
Adolphe imagines in the phrase: " If I had
loved her as she loved me " is quite unreal as
far as its relation to Ellenore's love is concerned. It means merely: " If I had loved her

a little more." Its content is limited entirely
by Adolphe's idea and capacity of love. If he
had loved her a little more, he thinks, then
they might have had a tranquil and placid
intrigue, passing by a decorous diminuendo to
friendly indifference. Ellenore would have
remained with the Count; the Count's suspicions would have been first lulled and then
forgotten while the flame peacefully burned
itself out.

No such development is conceivable with
Ellenore. It is Adolphe's impenetrable vanity
which makes him believe that Ellenore's sacrifices are made for the sake of holding him, and
that, if he had been a shade less impatient for
his freedom, she would not have made them.
But they are made because they have to be
made, at the imperious command of a love such
as he cannot conceive.

Again, one cannot tell how far Constant
was conscious and deliberate in this depiction
of Adolphe's insensitiveness and incomprehension. It is easy to say (as many critics do, at
least by implication) that he was simply describing himself, and that these had been his
thoughts in the same situation. But there is
no ground for believing that he was ever in the
same situation; and a similar situation is a
phrase without meaning. He may have drawn
out what was implicit in his own character into
Adolphe, and what was implicit in the
characters of women he had intimately known

into Ellenore; in Adolphe's case lowering, in Ellenore's heightening the reality, until it became a truly tragic contrast. But that is the work of a serious artist. Whether he was wholly conscious of all the effects, all the tragic irony, is a question as unanswerable as it is irrelevant. What author of a great book is? But to suppose that the power of the conception did not come from Constant's imagination, but that he stumbled upon it by a lucky accident of autobiography, seems to me quite unwarrantable; and it is still more unwarrantable to suggest that this supposition is confirmed by the fact that *Adolphe* is solitary among Constant's writings. I am not such a fool as to imagine that I could deduce from *Adolphe* that it was a solitary book; but I have no doubt that the impression it makes upon me is that it is the inspired effort of a man of genius, frustrated from cumulative achievement by a defect of character or " a sad lucidity of soul," to focus the quintessence of his experience in a creation which enabled him to reveal what he could not utter without falsity—the incessant struggle between demonic doubts and divine longings which he, as a person in the world of existence, could not resolve.

184

# CHAPTER V

Adolphe's vanity had deceived him completely. Ellenore breaks with the Count, not to hold him, but to be near him. He thinks it is only a threat, when it is already a reality. He tries to dissuade her—once again, not for the sake of her peace, but his own.

> "Listen!" she said. "If I break with the Count, will you refuse to see me? Will you refuse?" she repeated, seizing my arm with a violence which made me shudder.
>
> "No, assuredly no!" I replied. "And the unhappier you are, the more devoted I shall be. But think . . . ."
>
> "I have thought of everything," she interrupted. "He is coming back in a moment. Go away now; and do not come here again."

Again, the tragic irony. "The unhappier you are, the more devoted I shall be." It is the whole truth about Adolphe, and it is the sentence of death on Ellenore. But Adolphe is unconscious of the deeper meaning of his words. What he means, at this moment, by Ellenore's unhappiness is the consequences of her parting from the Count and casting aside her quasi-respectable security. But Ellenore's concern for respectability is past. She is a changed woman: she cares nothing now for this specious respectability. The power of love has uplifted and ennobled her. There is nothing intrinsic to her act of breaking with the Count which would make her unhappy:

quite the contrary. But as Adolphe sees her,
or wants to see her, she is a woman making
herself unhappy by rash and unconsidered
worldly sacrifices. To see her as she is—that
is, as a woman whose sacrifices, but for him,
would be the simplest acts of love, and would
make her happy, because they were commanded
of her by love, would be too alarming a vision.

Nevertheless, for a fleeting instant
Ellenore has her happiness. She has cast away
everything of the past; she now belongs,
visibly and invisibly, to Adolphe; she is a bride
preparing a home for love.

A woman brought me a note from Ellenore
begging me to go to see her in such and such a
house and street, on the third floor. I rushed
there, still hoping that, since she could not receive
me at the Count's house, she had made a rendezvous elsewhere for a last talk. I found her
preparing a permanent establishment. She came
to me, at once happy and shy, seeking to read my
thoughts in my eyes.

"Everything is broken off," she said. "I am
perfectly free. I have £75 a year of my own; it
is enough for me. You are staying here another
six weeks. When you leave, perhaps I can come
near you; perhaps you will come back to see me."
And, as though she would have dreaded a reply,
she plunged into a mass of details about her plans.
In every way she tried to persuade me that she
would be happy, that she had sacrificed nothing,
that what she had done was what she ought to have
done—quite apart from me.

It was plain that she was making a great effort
over herself, and that she only half-believed what
she was saying. She was bemusing herself with
her own words, for fear of hearing mine: she

busily spun out what she was saying to delay the
moment when my objections would plunge her
into despair again.  I could not find it in my heart
to make any.  I accepted her sacrifice, I thanked
her for it, I said it made me happy; I said a great
deal more: I assured her that I had always desired
that an irreparable decision would make it my
duty never to leave her; I attributed my waverings
to a feeling of delicacy which forbade me to consent to anything that would ruin her situation.  In
a word, my only thought was to drive far away
from her any hurt, any fear, any regret, any doubt
as to my feeling for her.  While I was speaking to
her, that was my only aim, and I was sincere in
my promises.

The passage is consummate.  It portrays
Ellenore at her most womanly, and Adolphe
at his most sensitive.  He is playing a part,
but he is constrained to it by genuine emotion,
and for a moment believes in his own sincerity.
It is only the more fatal for that.  We are left
to guess the real effect on Ellenore of his assurance that he had always desired that an
irreparable decision should make it his duty
never to leave her.  Its apparent simplicity is
equivocal.  Whose irreparable decision was it
to be?  Plainly, in the context and in Adolphe's
eyes, it is Ellenore's decision.  But Ellenore
could read it, and would be eager to read it,
as Adolphe's decision—the decision to love her
entirely, and to cleave to her in his soul.  As
she heard his words, did they mean to her that
he had desired to be bound by the obligation of
pity, or by the obligation of love?  In fact,
he had desired neither.  The obligation of love

he would have repudiated; the obligation of pity was transient and wholly emotional. He admitted it only because he felt it and for so long as he felt it, and struggled furiously against the memory of it when he did not. As for consciously desiring it, that was remote from him.

But Ellenore longed to believe; and his false assurance that his resistance to her openly leaving the Count had been inspired only by a feeling of delicacy—by the feeling that he must at all costs avoid bringing pressure upon her to take a step that would compromise her for ever, was one that would have deceived the elect; for freedom is the very gift of love. Ellenore could not but believe him, if she read him in his words alone. What she read in his voice and in his eyes may have been different.

If Ellenore believed, she could not believe for long. Adolphe's attitude towards the disapproval of society, and the even more hateful approbation of his cynical young acquaintances was one of embarrassment. Of the conviction of love, which could have withstood the one and despised the other, he had nothing: when it came to him it came too late.

> I am convinced that, if I had loved Ellenore, I should have won opinion over to her and me. Such is the power of true feeling that, when it speaks, false interpretations and artificial conventions are dumb. But I was only a weak man, grateful and dominated; I was not sustained by any impulsion that came from the heart.

188

The protecting aura of love, within which true lovers can live secure from the malice and incomprehension of the world and triumph over it, was never allowed to form itself about them. Ellenore was left exposed to contemptuous and insulting thoughts. " Solitude made her suffer; society made her blush."

> Ah, no doubt I should have consoled her; I should have clasped her against my heart and said: " Let us live for each other; let us forget those who cannot understand us; let us find all our happiness in our own esteem and love." I tried to do thus, but what power has a resolve taken by duty to rekindle a dying sentiment?

It was the obligation of pity: the obligation of love had never been felt at all. The obligation of love is not felt as an obligation, for it is the entry into freedom. But obligation, for Adolphe, is always a constriction of freedom. His deep desire is to be free of all obligation—to be absolutely free: which is, in fact, a condition of non-entity. Against the obligation of pity he is incessantly rebellious. To make his reluctant obedience to it appear like the surrender of love is impossible.

Therefore each has now to pretend with the other. Adolphe imagines that the reason why Ellenore does not speak to him of the hurts to which she is exposed, is because he had not asked for the sacrifice she had made. He is, as ever, superficial in his judgment of her. It is not the wounds themselves that she would

complain of, but the absence of that enveloping
atmosphere, which like the mist the gods
throw about their favourites in the Iliad, would
have made her invulnerable to such wounds.
The cause of her hurts is not her action, but
his lack of love. What is the good of confiding
that to him? Here, Constant gives a plain hint
that Adolphe came afterwards to realise the
truth which is now concealed from him. The
later Adolphe's declaration of his conviction
that, if he had truly loved Ellenore he would
have won opinion over to their side, is deliberate and forcible. We need not doubt the sincerity of his later faith that true love has the
power to silence false interpretations and artificial conventions. That is not quite the same
as the belief that he could have loved her truly.
What he thought about that we do not know;
and if we did, we should not be verily the wiser.
What a man thinks he might have done is never
half so convincing as what he actually did.

But at least the older Adolphe sees through
some of the illusions of the young one. He is
not to be deceived by his superficial understanding of Ellenore; and we may wonder
whether he was at all convinced by the younger
Adolphe's account of the beginning of dissimulation between himself and Ellenore.

> So we said nothing of the one thought which
> was in our minds. We were prodigal of caresses,
> we talked of love; but we talked of love for fear
> we might talk of something else.

What was the one thought that occupied their minds? The thing for fear of talking of which they talked of love? Was it, as Adolphe suggests, Ellenore's hurts, and his own belief that they were due to her own precipitancy and lack of prudence? Rather, simply his own lack of love.

> As soon as there is a secret between two loving hearts, as soon as one is resolved to hide from the other a single thought, the charm is broken, the happiness destroyed. Anger, injustice, even neglect, can be repaired; but dissimulation brings into love an alien element which denatures and blights it in its own eyes.

It is true; but dissimulation is nothing new on Adolphe's part by now. If there is anything new in the condition of dissimulation, it can only be that it is now mutual. Ellenore must have begun to hide her thoughts, whereas hitherto only Adolphe had hidden his.

That is indeed what has happened. After the episode of the duel and Adolphe's recovery, Ellenore makes no attempt to prevent or delay his return home; but she makes him promise either to come back to her, or let her come to him, in two months. He writes to her regularly, in his habitual fashion trying at first to tell, or to let transpire, the truth about his feelings, and then, apprehensive of the effect on Ellenore, ending with the language of love. " So, while never saying enough to satisfy her, I always said enough to impose upon her." Perhaps he was too confident of his skill. At

191

the end of the two months, since she knows he will not come to her, she prepares to come to him. In desperation, he resolves to tell her the truth; but his courage fails him, and he ends by proposing delay. Ellenore is deeply wounded, and sets off immediately.

> She let me know of her arrival. I went to her firmly resolved to show great joy; I was impatient to reassure her heart and bring her happiness or calm, at least for the moment. But she had been wounded; she examined me mistrustfully; she soon detected my efforts; she stung my pride by her reproaches; she insulted my character. She made my weakness appear so pitiable that I was angrier with her than with myself. A mad fury seized us; we flung aside all reserve, forgot all delicacy. We were hounded against each other by Furies.

In this anatomising of Adolphe to himself Ellenore's suppressed thought about him bursts out. She has seen him as he is, without illusion, before; but now she speaks what she sees, and that is a different matter. For a moment, Ellenore ceases to love him in his weakness. She is appalled by it and hates it. And he hates her for the truth she tells. But when the fury is over, he does not pretend she is equally to blame. It is his own words that haunt him, not hers. After all, she had told him nothing but the truth he knew; the horror had been that she told it to him.

After this fearful quarrel, for the first time he parts from her with no attempt at reconciliation.   Then he comes to his senses, and is appalled by the memory of his own words.   But before he can return to her he learns that his father has taken steps to have her expelled from the country.   He decides instantly to carry Ellenore away with him.   There is a violent revulsion in his soul.

> I formed endless projects for my everlasting reunion with Ellenore; I loved her more than I had ever loved her; my whole heart had returned to her; I was proud to protect her.   I was hungry to hold her in my arms; love entire had repossessed my soul; there was a fever in my head, my heart, my senses, which convulsed my existence.   If at that moment Ellenore had wanted to part from me, I would have died at her feet to hold her back.

It was true that Adolphe loved her " more than he had ever loved her."   It was not true that " love entire had repossessed his soul."   It never had possessed it.   What he experiences now is the same unfamiliar emotion he had experienced at Ellenore's surrender, but more intense and overwhelming.   There is the same mixture of tenderness and vanity.   Then it was for the bodily surrendered Ellenore; now it is for the socially helpless Ellenore.   It is a sense of triumph, mingled with a sense of pity, at her entire dependence upon him.

When their journey has begun, he seeks to persuade Ellenore that it is the rebirth of love.   He tells her that at his father's threat of separating them, he had realised that he could never be happy without her.   He had come to the sudden knowledge that his sole desire was to devote his life to her, and be completely united to her. But Ellenore, though she longs to be convinced, is not convinced. She makes him tell her the true story of what had happened. The fleeting moment of hope is past. Quietly and sadly she disillusions him.

> "Adolphe," she said, "you mistake yourself. You are generous, you devote yourself to me because I am persecuted; you think it is love, but it is only pity."
>
> Why did she speak these fatal words? Why did she reveal to me a secret I wanted to ignore? I strove to reassure her, and perhaps I succeeded; but the truth had passed through my soul: the emotion was destroyed. I was resolved in my sacrifice, but it no longer made me happy; and already there was in my mind a thought which I was again compelled to hide.

What Adolphe had wanted to believe, and did at times persuade himself to believe, is that he had experienced love for Ellenore; but it had died. Now, he wants to believe that the love had been reborn. But, even while he declares this to her, he knows it is untrue. He is "faking the record." What he had said to his father when he threatened to separate him from Ellenore by force majeure was: "Take care what you do. In thinking you are separating me from her, you may attach me to her for ever." But there is no need to appeal to this. The pattern of Adolphe is established and familiar. The deepest desire he knows is to be free from Ellenore, and that the liaison should come to an end; but, equally, he desires that it should end without pain for Ellenore, so that he should not be pained by her pain. That is to say, the deepest desire he knows is that Ellenore shall cease to love him, even as (he thinks) he has ceased to love her. But he has ceased to love her, because he never did love her; and she cannot cease to love him, because she really did love him. Because of this, it makes no difference to her love that the veils of her illusion about him are steadily withdrawn. She sees him as he is, and she loves him as he is.

Indeed, he is lovable. There is nothing else to do with Adolphe in the last resort, but to love him. The conflict between his craving to be loved, and his incapacity to love, is intolerable to a sympathetic understanding. He suffers, far differently from Ellenore; but his suffering is real. It is that of a man whose emotional nature cannot escape the tyranny of his intellect. He is a prisoner: and love, in Ellenore, longs to set him free. It is impotent to do so, and it becomes compassion, without ceasing to be love.

We shall therefore make a distinction between her compassion and his pity. Adolphe feels pity for Ellenore; it is overwhelming, and ultimately irresistible. "Deep in my soul I knew I could not have disobeyed her tears." But it is impotent to remove the cause of the tears: which is his lack of love. Ellenore on the other hand has compassion for Adolphe.

We may define this as the attitude of love towards the soul incapable of love, yet desirous to love. It is a form or mode of love. As Ellenore feels it towards Adolphe in the particular, so we may imagine God feeling it towards all human creatures. While Adolphe's pity is the manifestation of the desire to love, in a soul incapable of love.

It is harsh to see in Adolphe's pity for Ellenore only the selfish desire to spare himself the pain of her pain. In the last resort this is true, because the self is the frontier and limit of Adolphe's being: his definition is that he cannot escape from the self. But it is also true that by far the sharpest pain he feels is the pain of causing pain to Ellenore. This idiosyncrasy is not so common among men that we can afford to dismiss it as mere selfishness. Mankind is not so rich in love as that. Too many are unaffected by the tears they cause. It is the nearest approach to love in the soul incapable of love and desirous to love. Therefore it is no wonder that Adolphe mistakes it for love.

Nor is there any wonder that it is deadly. For if it is the nearest approach to love in the soul desirous to love, but incapable of love, Adolphe is compelled to seek it. And he will feel it most intensely towards the suffering which Ellenore endures for love of him. Her suffering is an agony because it springs from authentic love, which is love for him as he is,

and therefore in particular is love for that
which makes him peculiarly himself—namely
the combination and conflict of desire to love
and incapacity to love.   It is harsh and crude
to say that Adolphe desires that Ellenore shall
suffer; but he does desire to experience the pity
with which he emotionally responds to her
suffering.   The more intense her suffering, the
more overwhelming is his emotional response,
the more nearly it seems to approach to the
quality of authentic love: namely, that it is
" self-destroying " in Keats's sense of the word.
It seems to Adolphe, for example, when he suddenly rescues Ellenore from the ignominy of
expulsion, that his frigid, calculating, impatient, weary self is quite obliterated.   The
emotion is momentarily so overpowering that
he can almost believe it is love.

For this emotion he craves.   He may and
does tell himself that what he really desires is
that Ellenore should cease to love him; that she
should calmly and happily resume her place in
society and the even tenour of her life as it was
before he shattered it; that she should think of
him kindly, with affectionate friendship.   He
may and does tell himself that this desire is
very reasonable.   It has happened not infre-
quently that a liaison has declined peacefully
into unembittered indifference, even into un-
tumultuous affection.   He may and does tell
himself that it is obedience to the nature of
things for lovers thus to anticipate the inevi-

table death of love.    Nevertheless, it is impossible to imagine him acquiescing in such a turn of destiny.    He does not really desire that Ellenore should cease to love him.    That would be not only a mortal blow to his self-esteem, but something worse.    Indeed, it was precisely because he sensed that Ellenore was incapable of a casual liaison, or indeed of any love but an enduring one, that he had sought to win her.    And he had won her because she responded to the vibration of suffering in his soul, the tension between the desire to love and the incapacity to love.    Her love had recognised him and given him a validity which he had never possessed.    If she ceased to love him, he would be condemned to non-entity.    But it is only in some dim region of his soul that he is aware of this.

It is at this point that Adolphe escapes the ironical analysis of Constant's preface to the Third Edition (1824), where he speaks of the men who had told him that they had been in precisely Adolphe's situation, victims of the immense love conceived for them, and comments dryly: " For the most part I think they calumniated themselves and if their vanity had left them undisturbed, their conscience could have been at peace." This is the same analysis which, as we shall see, the Baron will bring to bear on Adolphe: but, if only by a hair's breadth, it misses the mark.    Not only because Ellenore's love for Adolphe is entire, and would not cease if Adolphe were purged of vanity, but only become happy. But there has always been something besides vanity in Adolphe's desire for love. It is not only the bad desire for self-importance part of it is the nobler longing to be validated by love. He will only know this for what it is, when it is humanly too late. Now he has only an obscure sense of it, which makes him cling—not only for pity's sake—to Ellenore. Constant's irony is true. There are not many Adolphes, and those who think they are like him had better beware of giving themselves away.

Adolphe would undergo a more intimate annihilation than that of his self-esteem if Ellenore ceased to love him. Equally, he would undergo annihilation of another kind— were he to love her as she loves him: that is, without thought of self, because she is herself only in loving him. But liberation from the self in love is impossible for Adolphe. The nearest he comes to it is momentary self-obliteration by a wave of pity. But since it is the self—the egotistic, calculating, intellectual part—which is the cause of the distress which he pities, the wave of emotion is merely a wave which recedes and reveals the self unchanged. Adolphe's pity is the sudden, momentary, and always defeated revolt of his heart against the tyranny of his mind. But Ellenore's pity is constant and unchanging; it is an overflowing of love. And love is not only an emotion; it is also a knowledge, in which mind and heart are integrated and at one. Ellenore knows Adolphe, as Adolphe never knows her; indeed she knows him as he never knows himself, for she sees in him the man unborn and " powerless to be born." Her pity is compassion.

This distinction between Adolphe's pity and Ellenore's compassion does more justice to him than the former distinction between true and spurious pity. To call Adolphe's pity spurious suggests that it was easily within his power to remove the cause of the distress that he pities, and that he refused to do it. It was not easily within his power; it required an inward revolution—a spiritual rebirth.

But that his unconscious craving for the momentary and deceptive liberation from the self which he experiences when he is overwhelmed by pity is deadly, admits no doubt. It brings his impregnable self continually within the " magnetic field " of Ellenore's love. The contact of pity from his emotional nature reanimates her love, even against her deeper knowledge, on the plane of hope and expectation of earthly union; it is always followed by the withdrawal of his unchanged intellectual self, stubborn in its assertion of freedom and its denial of the enduringness of love. This attraction and repulsion is like the intake and output of a bellows on the fire that is consuming Ellenore within. The forced draught roars away her life.

Prophetically, finally, Ellenore *knows* that Adolphe's love is only pity, and that it can never become compassion. But she clings to life, as a loving woman must. What she knows will kill her; and she knows that it will. But she cannot live on that plane of knowledge. Not until she is dead can she be all soul. The rest of the story is the story of the unavailing struggle of the living woman against her doom. It is lit by flashes of hope, darkened by foreknowledge, until the certainty of death brings with it the approach of calm and peace.

# CHAPTER VI

Adolphe and Ellenore, after the flight, settle in a little town in Bohemia. For a while he resolutely sets himself to conceal his longing for freedom. One day she receives from the Count a letter offering her one half of the fortune to which he has now been restored, on the sole condition that she leaves Adolphe. She decides to refuse, and tells Adolphe. It straightway becomes an act of virtue on his part to leave her, and he determines to tell her that he loves her no longer. He manages to say as much. She faints, and he lies.

> "Ellenore!" I cried. "Come back to yourself! Come back to me! I love you—truly and tenderly. I told you false to make you freer in your choice!"

It is very like what he said when she decided to leave the Count (Ch. IV); and as before she half believes him.

> The credulity of the heart is inexplicable! These simple words, belied by so many before, restored Ellenore to life and confidence. She made me repeat them several times, she seemed eager to breathe. She believed me; she was intoxicated by her own love, which she took for ours; she confirmed her reply to the Count, and I was more deeply committed than ever.

As always, Adolphe exaggerates the credulity of Ellenore. It is only superficial, for the doubt in her soul is ineradicable. It quickly emerges again. News comes to her

202

that her father, who has been an exile in Russia
since her babyhood, has been restored to his
estates in Poland.   He presses her to return.
Adolphe espies a new hope of freedom.   But
Ellenore tells him outright that she will not
return unless he goes with her.

> " If there is something hard in my resolve,
> Adolphe, you must blame yourself.   If I could
> have any illusion about you, I might consent to
> our parting; because its bitterness would be
> diminished by the prospect of a sweet and lasting
> reunion.   But you would ask nothing better than
> to believe I was six hundred miles away from you,
> happy and at peace, in the midst of my family
> and surrounded by wealth.   Then you would write
> me such reasonable letters; I can see them now;
> they would tear my heart to pieces.   I do not want
> to expose myself to that. . . ."
> There was a kind of roughness and violence in
> Ellenore's voice and tone which indicated a firm
> determination rather than a deep or touching
> emotion.

Truly, Adolphe had deceived himself about
her credulity.   Perhaps for a moment Ellenore
may seem unsympathetic; but not when we
remember the foreknowledge that haunts her.
She is going to die, and all the woman in her
longs that Adolphe shall be with her to the end
and at the end.   Though she suffers terribly
from his coldness when they are together, she
would suffer far worse if there were six
hundred miles between them.   The tortured
happiness of his presence and his pity is better
than the numb coldness of distance.

Since Adolphe is reluctant to go to Poland,

Ellenore does not go, and they linger on in Bohemia. He is just about to give way when her father dies, leaving her sole, but disputed, heiress to his property. If she intends to secure her title to it she must go. Since it is essential to Adolphe's plan of freedom that Ellenore shall be materially secure, he goes with her. He receives an ironical letter from his father, recommending him to his country's minister in Poland—the Baron.

Adolphe goes to see the Baron, who straightway becomes a prime agent in the drama. He is cynical and worldy wise, and has been well posted in Adolphe's affairs by Adolphe's father. We shall understand his part in the drama best, if we envisage him as a projection of the intellectual part of Adolphe's divided being. What two-thirds of Adolphe believes, the Baron believes wholly. He is Adolphe without the inhibition, or the redeeming grace, of his emotions; he says outright what Adolphe's intellectual part would like to say, does what it would like to do. This does not prevent him from being entirely convincing as a character in his own right. Quite the contrary: for an Adolphe, purged of his inclination and aptitude to be overwhelmed by pity, would be a much more 'solid' person. From the point of view of art, the Baron is a magnificent invention. By means of him, while keeping himself entirely within the bounds of strictly realistic probability, Constant endows the mental part of Adolphe with the power of decisive action.

At the first encounter, the Baron, with genuine sympathy, tells Adolphe the truth of his situation.

> "There is not a man who has not known, once in his life, what it is to be torn between the desire to break an unsuitable liaison and the fear of hurting the woman he has loved. The inexperience of youth vastly exaggerates the difficulties of such a situation; it is inclined to believe in the truth of all those demonstrations of suffering which take the place of the weapons of strength and reason in the weaker and more excitable sex. One's heart may suffer, but one's self-esteem is gratified; and the man who, in all good faith, believes he is sacrificing himself to the despair he has caused, is in fact sacrificing himself only to the illusions of his own vanity. The world is full of passionate women: every one of them has cried that she would die if she were abandoned; every one of them is still alive, and has found consolation."

The Baron's wisdom is à la Rochefoucauld. He understands Adolphe, or two-thirds of him, only too well. Ellenore is quite beyond him. Such creatures do not exist in the world of reality. To him her premonition of death would be nonsense; the idea of her complete surrender to love fantastic. Belief in either is an indulgence of a young man's vanity. Let Adolphe break with her, and Ellenore will quickly cease to suffer and find another man. And Adolphe himself will be the better man for having done so, for is it not self-evidently good to cease to indulge the illusions of vanity?

It is all sound: on one assumption—that love is not what it is, and Ellenore not what she is. Since the greater part of Adolphe shares that assumption, the Baron is only putting clearly what most of Adolphe himself believes, and undermining the part which does not quite believe it. That part is (he says) merely vanity. And the Baron, on his own assumption, is subtle as well as sound. " If you still loved her, you would not have come to me. . . . It was easy for you to guess what I had to say to you." That Adolphe had listened to it calmly was the proof of its truth.

Whereby, of course, the Baron admits the existence of a condition which he calls love. He would define it precisely as Adolphe himself had defined it to Ellenore in the previous chapter.

> " But love—that transport of the senses, that involuntary intoxication, that oblivion of every interest and every duty—I have it no longer, Ellenore."

The Baron and Adolphe are really at one. In such a condition, the Baron says, Adolphe would not have come to him, or listened to him without anger. That he has come and listened quietly is the proof that he is no longer in it, Adolphe has not only admitted this to himself, but declared it plainly to Ellenore. Only Adolphe, overcome by pity of Ellenore's distress, had promptly repudiated his words. That is the sole difference between Adolphe as he is, and the Adolphe whom the Baron sees, whose soul he can read (he says) better than Adolphe himself. From him, Adolphe as he is differs only by his propensity to be carried away by pity into lying to Ellenore about his feelings.

This difference, says the Baron, is based on illusion. Adolphe's pity is aroused by the spectacle of a suffering which is not real; or if real, is only superficial and transitory. Two things therefore conspire to make Adolphe refuse the truth, and thus be untrue to himself. One is Ellenore's pretence of suffering unto death; the other is Adolphe's vanity which makes him want to believe that the pretence is true.

The Baron's probe goes deep. Does Adolphe want to believe that Ellenore will die without him? Assuredly, he does. The dependence of her life upon his love is the only proof, convincing to himself, of his own validity and worth. (Constant said of himself: " I am not quite a real person ": it is of his 'reality' in this sense that Ellenore's love is evidence to Adolphe). But is this vanity? The true analysis is not so simple. At least it has to be made on a higher plane than the Baron's conception of vanity. Adolphe is beset by a problem which has no meaning in the Baron's philosophy—the problem of his own spiritual identity, or intrinsic worth. For the Baron all that is settled by the position one achieves or is born to in the world of society. A man is worth what he will fetch: the esteem and emolument that accrue to him from his position in the social hierarchy. The Baron may be, perhaps is, inwardly sceptical about it all; but in the last resort the judgment of the established order of society is final and admits no appeal. A man *is* what society considers him to be; his worth *is* what society values him at.

Two-thirds of Adolphe agrees; but his other part is recalcitrant. His other part is travailed, in spite of himself, by the different and incommensurable question: What am I worth, *in myself*? This is a religious question: probably the one and only religious question, in the sense that it is *the* question to which the Christian religion is an answer. For the only assurance mortal man can ever have that he possesses intrinsic worth is the assurance that he is loved by a superior being. This assurance may come to him in either of two ways (which do not exclude each other): he may be assured that he is loved by God, or he may be assured that he is loved by a superior human being. In fact, the first of these, as affirmed by the Christian religion, is not very different from the second. For the love of God is mediated and revealed to the Christian believer through the personal love of Jesus for him. Looking upon the Cross—*respiciamus donec respiciet*\*— he knows that Jesus laid down his life for love

* "Let us look back at him till he looks back at us," quoted by Lancelot Andrewes in a sermon.

of him.   Not otherwise, essentially, does the man like Adolphe, who is incapable of this Christian belief, receive the assurance of his own worth and reality in the knowledge that an Ellenore will lay down her life for love of him.

To the third part of Adolphe, therefore, Ellenore's love has a meaning clean outside the range of the Baron's philosophy.   This part of him desires above all else to be loved.   And this desire is not vanity, but the spiritual desire to *be*; and to be, in being known.   To gather this spiritual desire under the rubric of vanity is to degrade and denature it.   True, it assumes an equivocal form in Adolphe.   It is divided against itself and corrupted by the presence of vanity.   It is vanity, in part, that makes him want to believe that Ellenore cannot live without him; but it is not vanity at all that makes him want to believe that she will lay down her life for him.   And the difference between these two things lies in the difference between two planes on which he experiences Ellenore.   There is an Ellenore who is the passive victim of a hopeless love inspired by his notion of himself: an Ellenore whom he pities and on whose dependence he plumes himself.   This Ellenore is, in isolation from the second one, a figment of Adolphe's vanity.   The Baron is right; and his probe touches the quick of the Adolphe who thus conceives her.   But the second Ellenore, who is the veritable and ately sacrifices first all the values of this world, spiritual Ellenore, is the woman who deliber- and then her own life, in obedience to her love for Adolphe as he really is.   This Ellenore is, so to speak, the mistress of her destiny, or would be, were it not that she has deliberately surrendered all to love.   But that is the same thing to one who believes, as she believes, in love " in whose service is perfect freedom." This Ellenore we see clearly : but Adolphe sees her only dimly, through the mist of his own vanity.   But he is not entirely blind to her.   He could see her clearly only with the vision of love, which he can in no wise attain.   He sees her only through a glass, darkly.   But what he does see makes nonsense of the Baron's cynicism.

It is the part of him which sees the true Ellenore which is stung to utterance by the Baron's words.   Because the two parts of Adolphe have spoken so clearly and ruthlessly through the Baron, the third part is aroused to a protest and a declaration of faith such as it would never have made if the dialogue had been purely inward.   This is psychologically true. When another speaks to a man the thoughts of one side of his divided being, he is instantly in arms and becomes the advocate of the other side, with an exaggerated conviction, of which the excess derives from resentment that the other has penetrated his secret.   It is neither pleasant nor good to be known, except in the

spirit of love. The Baron neither would nor
could pretend to that. He means well, indeed;
but to mean well is not to love. That they
" mean well " is the judgment of love on those
who do ill, not knowing what they do. The
Baron means well, in that he desires to guide
Adolphe towards what he believes to be good,
namely, the " glittering prizes " of the God of
this world. But these are the false goods of a
false God. If the Baron had been touched by
the spirit of love he could not believe in them.

So the third part of Adolphe is instantly
in arms, resentful of the Baron's knowledge of
his secret; and he proclaims, on behalf of his
third part, a faith in which he cannot believe.

> " I thought it my duty, sir," I replied, " to
> listen to you in silence; but I owe it to myself to
> make plain that you have not shaken me. I
> repeat, only I can judge Ellenore; nobody else ap-
> preciates the truth of her sentiments and the depth
> of her feelings. As long as she needs me, I shall
> stay with her. No kind of success could ever con-
> sole me for having left her unhappy; and if my
> career were to be confined to giving her something
> to lean on, to supporting her in her sufferings, to
> protecting her by my affection from the injustice
> of a world which misunderstands her, I should still
> believe my life had not been wasted."

It was well said. Adolphe proclaims the
values of the spiritual world against those of
the material one: the service of God against
the service of Mammon. He alone knows, he
says, the nature and quality of Ellenore's love;
he, therefore, alone knows the nature and

quality of the injustice done to it by the opinion of the world which, like the Baron who speaks for it, believes that because it is not " legitimate " it must be superficial and transient. By remaining faithful to her, by making that his life's purpose, his life will be wasted in the judgment of the world, but justified in his own.

Here, for a fleeting moment, Adolphe's pity becomes authentic. He may not claim for himself the radiance of love; but he does assert his faith in loyalty to the purity of Ellenore's love for him. If he cannot reciprocate it in kind, he can and will acknowledge his obligation to it, as something higher than himself, which he can recognise and to which he will respond in the best way he can. And if he does, he knows that his life will not have been wasted.

But the misery is that Adolphe has used the part of himself which half-believes all this merely as an advocate to defend himself against the Baron's discovery of him. His words are mere heroics, because it is the unchanged Adolphe who has spoken them: the Adolphe whose verity the Baron has unmasked. The Adolphe who could make them true, and not heroics, would be an Adolphe resolved to act in accord with his pretended faith. This Adolphe he must will into reality. He does not even make the attempt. " But how explain the fickleness by which the sentiment that inspired the words faded even before I had finished speaking them?" Adolphe asks. We have explained it.

What now reverberates in his mind is not his own assertion of the values of the spiritual world, but the Baron's assertion of the values of the material one. " Between you and every kind of success there is one obstacle—and that obstacle is Ellenore." It is about this that all his thoughts and desires crystallise; the brave declaration is dead at birth.

With a masterly hand Constant now depicts this crystallisation of the total Adolphe about the idea of Ellenore as the obstacle. First, she is merely the obstacle to Adolphe's taking his rightful place in the Baron's world. Now he accepts that world without demur; but in accepting it he transforms it, by magic, from a world of limitation to one of unlimited freedom.

> It was not only one career I regretted; having attempted none, I regretted them all. Having never made trial of my powers, I imagined them unlimited and cursed them.

Then he transmutes the Baron's world still further by making it a realm of love. He has visions of an " ideal mate " within it. This " legitimate " love of his dream would have the immeasurable advantage of making him independent, even in his love. And how much more loving he would be!

> If only heaven had granted me a woman whom convention allowed me to acknowledge, whom my father would not blush to accept as his daughter,

> how much happier I should have been to make her
> happy. My tenderness is misunderstood because
> it is wounded and suffers; it is imperiously sum-
> moned to produce evidences of itself, and my heart
> refuses them to passion and threats. How sweet
> it would be to surrender to it with the beloved
> being, the companion of a regular and respected
> life! . . . . I have made all these sacrifices without
> the call of duty or love—do they not prove what
> I could do at their call?

Adolphe's eyes "filled with tears." They
well might, since he had succeeded in reconcil-
ing completely the service of God and Mammon
in this kingdom of success and virtue and
married bliss, from which Ellenore keeps him
an exile. His mind is flooded with memories
of childhood.

> I was reduced to repelling the sweetest mem-
> ories and the most natural longings as though they
> were criminal thoughts. But the companion whom
> my fancy had suddenly created was in harmony
> with all these memories, and made all these long-
> ings legitimate; she shared all my duties, my
> pleasures and my tastes; she joined my present life
> to the period of my youth when hope displayed a
> boundless future before me—a period from which
> Ellenore had separated me by an abyss.

There follows a conventional romantic
picture of the landscape of his childhood—René
a t   s e c o n d - h a n d—emphatically belying
Adolphe's claim that the tiniest details were
painfully vivid. "And my fantasy set beside
them a young and innocent girl who made them
more beautiful and alive with hope."

So Adolphe takes refuge in a fantasy in
which the feigned innocence of childhood disin-

fects the Baron's world, and the bitch-goddess success is endowed with the glamour of maiden love. The psychological subtlety of this piece of art is admirable. The Baron's world is metamorphosed into an earthly paradise, in which all Adolphe's conflicting desires are simultaneously satisfied, and love and ambition lie down together like the lamb and the lion " in happy copulation "; and Ellenore is the devil with the flaming sword who shuts him out.

Never had Adolphe sunk quite so low. Better, much better, was the naked antagonism of ambition and emotion than this monstrous generation from their union. But the art and the truth are notable. The pitiful descent follows immediately after the heroic flight. Never had he soared so high; never had he fallen so low. Baron Mephistopheles has won a signal victory.

It is not without a tinge of anti-romantic irony that Adolphe, after wandering in this fantasy of romance and respectability, is represented as escaping from the shock of reality into a more authentic romantic rêverie, as the night closes in upon him. He has the familiar " sensation of immensity."

It was long since I had experienced anything like this. Everlastingly absorbed in personal reflections, my eyes always fixed on my own situation, I had become a stranger to impersonal ideas. I was occupied only with Ellenore and myself— with Ellenore who inspired only pity and weariness in me, with myself whom I now despised. I had shrunk into a new kind of egotism—egotism without courage, malcontent and humiliated. I was thankful to become alive to thoughts of a different order, to find myself once more capable of forgetting myself, and surrendering to disinterested meditations. My soul seemed to rouse up from a long and shameful degradation.

The experience of night passes into a meditation on death—"the certain end which neither consoles nor calms us." Adolphe makes it do both, for the time being. What (he muses) is the sense of ambition? Why be a victim to the delusion that his wasted years are really wasted? If they were filled with the success of ambition, they would be wasted just as much in the end. "I spread unhappiness round me to recapture a few wretched years which time will soon snatch from me."

It is an escape into indifference: into the philosophy which inspired his liaison and poisoned his love. This indifference is also manifestly the midway point, the *punctum indifferens*, between the Adolphe who agrees with the Baron that his life is wasted and the Adolphe who heroically defies him and declares that his life will not be wasted if he serves Ellenore to the end. Though it is no escape, for he cannot maintain in the life of action and commitment the indifference it counsels, it is at least much more dignified than the vapid and corrupt day-dream it has displaced. We are at liberty to believe that it was for this in

216

particular that he despised himself and felt his degradation. It is probable that an Adolphe would.

At any rate he has returned to his own basis. Now the false heroics of loyalty to the nobility of Ellenore's love, and the still falser and more cowardly vision of her as the evil genius who bars him from an earthly paradise, are both alien to him. He has regained a momentary integrity. It is very precarious. The mere fact that Ellenore, racked with anxiety at his sudden disappearance, has sent out the villagers to look for him irritates him as an encroachment on his freedom. But he manages to subdue his irritation, and is " moved by her emotion."

The calm of indifference induced by his meditation on death is deplorably short-lived. It lasts precisely one long night of sleep. The next day the day-dream is triumphant, and so it remains. Sensitive to the change in him, Ellenore seeks to know the cause. He tells her nothing, and she sets a friend to discover the secret. At first Adolphe piques himself on giving no clear indication that he is not in love with Ellenore. But her friend is sympathetic to Adolphe, and inclined to *Schadenfreude.*

> I was drawn on to make a clean breast of my feelings. I avowed that I felt devotion, sympathy, pity for Ellenore; but I added that love had nothing to do with the duties I imposed upon myself.

It is a good deal less than a complete confession.   Adolphe would be too ashamed of his day-dream—or compulsive feminine image—to make a clean breast of that.   But the friend's account of what he had confessed was enough to wound Ellenore to the quick.   She reacts impulsively: she sets herself to fill her house with society, then to flirt in the hope of reviving his love.   And Adolphe is at first blind enough to believe she is serious, and spies a hope of freedom in the waning of her love.   With the prospect of the end before him, he becomes gentler in his manner towards her.   But his acquiescence in her flirtations proves his indifference, and she flings herself more desperately into them.   He is indifferent still.   Her friends are understandably indignant, with his apparent combination of devotion and levity. Adolphe is indignant at their indignation.

> My reward for my years of devotion was to be misunderstood and slandered.   I had forgotten all the interests and rejected all the pleasures of life for a woman, and it was I who was condemned.

Yet   the   rough   judgment   was   just. Adolphe's devotion, which looked to the outer world like love, was now nearer to hate.   And the interests and pleasures he plumed himself on having forgotten and rejected he had not forgotten or rejected at all.   The seductive feminine image was continually before his mind; and Ellenore was the only obstacle to possession.

But that is his secret.   On the face of

things he can pretend a grievance at an injustice, which no doubt he sincerely felt to be
unjust at the moment of his protesting elo-
quence. Ellenore banishes her suitors,
instantly. With no non-conducting body
between them they are only the more unhappy.
Now his hatred finds tongue.

> I stopped only when I saw Ellenore in tears,
> and even her tears were only a burning lava which,
> falling drop by drop on my heart, forced cries
> from me, but never a disavowal. Then, more than
> once, I saw her rise, pale and prophetic.
>
> "Adolphe!" she cried, "you do not know the
> evil you do; you will learn one day, you will learn
> it from me, when you have driven me into the
> grave."
>
> Woe is me that I did not, when she spoke, cast
> myself into the grave before her!

The chapter that ends with these words is
magnificent. It depicts the working out of the
effect of the Baron upon Adolphe's soul. He
has conjured up in it the feminine image which
corrupts what remains of genuine loyalty in
Adolphe, so that his love turns into hatred.
Then the actual destruction of Ellenore begins.
What was presentiment and foreknowledge of
the soul becomes a force of bodily dissolution.
Ellenore begins to feel death in her body, for
those vestiges of love which were in his devotion, and on which her life was fed, are now
turned to the image which reigns in Adolphe's
heart.

Then Ellenore tells him the truth, not to
his face, but in a letter which she leaves for

him to read after her death. " You have frozen
me with fear," she wrote.

> " Must I die then, Adolphe? Well, you will
> be satisfied. She will die—the poor creature you
> protected, but whom you strike again and again.
> She will die—the troublesome Ellenore whom you
> cannot bear to be near you, whom you look on
> as an obstacle, for whom you cannot find a spot
> on earth that does not weary you. She will die:
> you will walk alone in the midst of the crowd you
> are impatient to join. You will come to know them
> —these men to whom you are now grateful for
> their indifference. And perhaps one day, when
> you are wounded by these unfeeling hearts, you
> will regret the heart of which you were the lord,
> which lived on your affection, which would have
> braved every danger to defend you, and which you
> no longer deign to reward with a look."

Had her love been turned into fear? No:
for it is true that perfect love casts out fear, and
her love was perfect. But the love which is
perfect and unafraid may pray that the cup will
pass. She is afraid of her own fearful suffering at his harshness; afraid of the enemy who
strikes her through his words. Of death itself
she is unafraid; she will invoke it as the
deliverer. But of the Adolphe whose love has
turned to hatred, and who is killing her, she
is in terror.

# CHAPTER VII

The Baron returns to work. Now, instead of the idea of the world of Mammon which has produced its effect in Adolphe, he gives him the reality. He chooses a company for Adolphe to shine in, and Adolphe shines. He gives him work to do, to whet the appetite of his ambition. For a moment, its partial satisfaction quietens Adolphe. In the Baron's company he takes *le ton de la maison* in regard to Ellenore. What a business it is to get rid of a mistress one is resolved to discard! He is in the toil. The Baron invites him to a reception to which, as he suavely tells him, the reigning beauties of Poland will be invited, but Ellenore for obvious reasons cannot be. Adolphe swallows the hook and goes; his disloyalty to Ellenore is now entire.

At the reception, the eyes of all are upon him. There is whispered conversation about him. He is painfully embarrassed. The Baron comes to the rescue and pays him particular attention; and when the company has departed, keeps him back to reopen the subject of Ellenore. Astutely, he strikes while the iron is hot. It is made hotter still by the arrival of a note from Ellenore, anxious at his delay. Adolphe receives it in the Baron's presence and is stung by his pitying smile.

"Yes," I cried. "I will give you my promise to break with Ellenore. [I will fulfil it in three days.]  I will tell her myself.  You can write to tell my father in advance."

He rushes away, only half-believing in his own promise, to find that Ellenore has become suspicious of his commerce with the Baron.  He denies everything, and Ellenore persuades herself once more.  The three days pass and he has done nothing except to write to the Baron at the last minute to ask for more time and to assure him that from now on it could be taken for granted that he had broken with Ellenore for ever.

Having thus, as he thinks, postponed the necessity of action, Adolphe gives himself up to the last refinement of the sensation which he savours above all others.  Certain that the end is at hand, he is free to be tender to Ellenore.  Now he seeks the conversations he has avoided; now he takes delight in her words of love which irritated him before.  Now, they are precious: each one of them may be the last.  And Ellenore's wounded heart is assuaged.

The hypocrisy would be diabolical indeed, were it not that in Adolphe's divided mind the action of finally breaking with Ellenore is never real.  It is never something he has done, irrevocably, in the world of act and deed— what Amiel called " l'engrenage terrible de la responsabilité et de la souffrance humaine."  Into that fearful machinery Adolphe will never willingly put his hand.  He lives, so to speak, in a world of infinite freedom in which

thoughts and words take the place of deeds.
Thoughts and words, he feels rather than
thinks, are always revocable, always obliter-
able. To desire the end, to think the end, to
imagine the end: this is one thing. To will
the end, to make the end: this is quite another.
The one is permissible, the other dreadful. The
end must come like death, from beyond, by the
nature of things, and he will be its passive
instrument, not its active agent.

The secret of Adolphe's nature lies herein.
It derives from the idea of death which has
dominion over him. That it is by a permission
of his will that the idea of death has this dominion does not enter his head. To him the
dominion of the idea of death is as obvious and
self-evident as the fact of death. What astonishes him is men's refusal to recognise it. This
comes, he believes, from a radical insensitiveness, or lack of imagination. And this astonishment is justified. Not to have felt the
dominion of death is not to have awakened to
the reality of life. Fully conscious living must
begin with an awareness of death; and it ad-
vances through a struggle for victory over the
idea of death.

To the soul aware of death, the choice of
two freedoms is offered. There is the freedom
to be won by allowing death to have
dominion. If we enthrone death as the final
end, we are driven to conclude that all values
are annihilated. They are gathered up, in-

distinguishable, into the darkness. The essential fact of all experience is that it is transitory, and unmeaning. Any significance we attach to experience is really an illusion. If we wish to behave as though it were significant, we must do so, in order not to be dupes, as men who choose to abide by the rules of the game, although they know it is merely a game. The stakes are quite imaginary : worthless counters. But we can play, if we will, for the fun of the thing. And a sense of freedom comes from this.

Another and an opposite freedom is won by overcoming the idea of death. As an idea this is simple enough. All it requires is that we should be convinced of the significance of experience. But this conviction can be achieved only through experiences which are themselves transcendent. Of these the chief are the experiences of duty and love. And the experience of duty must be subsumed under that of love. For obedience to an obligation which depends on an external sanction—such as punishment by the law, or for that matter by God himself —is not the transcendent experience of duty. Duty fulfilled for its own sake is duty fulfilled for love. True love and true duty are never discrepant. In the act of recognising them as the will of a higher power we enter a realm of freedom, in which the dominion of death is destroyed.

To accept the dominion of death is to be

impenetrable to the summons of duty and love: for to be responsive to their summons is to recognise them as transcendent, and oneself as partly transcendent in virtue of that "fine point" of the soul which recognises and obeys it. But the dominion of death spreads over all existence a twilight in which the transcendent cannot be discerned. The freedom which it gives, being the freedom of the uniform and valueless and illimitable, is a delusion. It is the freedom to serve nothing, which turns to slavery.

Of this slavery Adolphe is the victim. He is enslaved by the false freedom bestowed by the dominion of death. Seeking this freedom, he recoils from commitment and obligation as, in themselves, intolerable. This is the root of his growing hatred of Ellenore. He recoils from the commitment with which love threatens him through her. But he recoils equally from the commitment to tell her the truth and make an end. The consequence is that the end, which he makes by not making it, is more terrible: he becomes the instrument of death. For to refuse commitment is to be committed—to death: to become the servant of the power of death.

The subtlety of Constant is the more impressive, because it appears so simple. With the death of his love impending, Adolphe feels free: free, at last, to take delight in love. It is, in fact, a deathly perversion of love: love made exquisitely delightful by the denial of its own transcendence and eternity. In this experience the philosophy of Adolphe attains its consummation. And he feels this freedom to delight in dying love, because with some infinitely tenuous thread of his being he can say that he has not actively willed the death of love. He has anticipated it, but he has not willed it. Or, if he has willed it, he has granted a reprieve. The death of love is not his act. It is a metaphysical necessity. One does not consent to such a necessity, one submits to it.

This philosophical conviction is the original source of Adolphe's attitude, and a sufficient trace of it clings to him to make him something less than diabolical. There is a point in his soul where he is contemplative and, as it were disembodied: the passive spectator of the transitory life which ends absolutely in the nothingness of death. This might be well if the contemplative part had governed the whole of him, and he had withdrawn from life. But he had deliberately sought the human relation of love in order to escape his loneliness and to assure himself of his own reality. He forsook the attitude of contemplation: understandably enough, for it was sterile. Contemplation which does not culminate in the knowledge of love is barren and deathly. But while he flees from the bitterness of his contemplation, he does not disavow it. It governs his attitude towards the love into which he escapes. He imposes his own terms upon the experience. It also must be transitory. Thus he forces the experience of love under the dominion of death. The closer his contact with Ellenore's faith that love transcends death and creates a bond which outlasts death, the fiercer becomes his struggle against her. It is a struggle to prevent his faith in the dominion of death from being overthrown by hers in the dominion of love.

He is struggling to maintain what he mistakenly believes to be his integrity of thought against her integrity of feeling. The allies he enlists in the struggle: ambition, convention, and the fantasy of a love which reconciles them both, are a stage army. They are irrelevant to the spiritual struggle, because Adolphe does not believe in them. They are mere counters in the futile game of life. It is true that, if his philosophy prevails, this is all life can be. On that assumption the values of " this world " are the natural allies of the philosophy of death. But value in themselves they cannot have. Adolphe can only pretend they have. And something in himself revolts at the pretence. In a fit of final exasperation against Ellenore, he has subscribed to them, by giving the Baron his promise to break with her. But he evades his promise. And he uses the freedom gained by this evasion to regain the attitude that is indefeasibly his own—the pitiful contemplation of love under the shadow of death.

Constant, in his habit as he lived, was an inveterate gambler at the tables. When one first studies his life it appears a strange aberration that one so gifted should have spent so much of his life in this pursuit; and that the "passion"—to give it its conventional description, although it is hardly appropriate to Constant—should have steadily increased its hold upon him. But when one comes to consider all that is revealed in *Adolphe* concerning the nature of the man who conceived and wrote the story, it appears fitting that his philosophy should have found expression in play. Only thus could he utter his conviction that the life of this world was a futile game. Gambling was, so to speak, his form of religion. The gaming table was his altar: except that he did not worship there; he worshipped nothing; he could find nothing to worship. The gaming table was the *ersatz*-altar of his devoutly irreligious soul: the symbol of the interminable and irreconcilable conflict that went on within.

Saint-Beuve tells the story that shortly before the publication of his book on religion (1825) someone met Constant in a gaming-house and asked him what he was busy on at the moment. "Only on religion," was the reply.

By his assiduity at the gaming-table Constant expressed at once his contempt for and his allegiance to the values of this world. He played with a cold clarity of mind, in a kind of willing unison with what he conceived to be the nature of things. Had he been a more ruthless man, he would have played with the lives of others in the same spirit. But his genuine tenderness of heart made him incapable of this.

Constant the gambler, and Constant the artist, are thus blood brothers. But they are not identical. One could almost deduce the actual gambler from the spirit which brooded over the creation of *Adolphe*. But the spirit moves in a world of essences, and is itself essence. Constant the gambler is existence. And essence is never wholly embodied in existence. There is that in *Adolphe* which Constant could never express in any action save that of art. It contains the inexpressible secret of his soul: so that we feel the inward verity of which the gambling was only a clumsy and partial symbol, and to which even the confessions of the *Journal Intime* afford only a clue.

Nevertheless, the gambling of Constant is truly significant. First, because it is the appropriate expression in an action of this world of Adolphe's philosophy, which makes the pursuit of ambitions of this world a futile game, yet derides an aim beyond them. Practised by a highly conscious, highly intelligent and clairvoyant man like Constant, it implies a withering criticism of the decisive value of this world, which is money. It asserts a derisive complicity with the world in which, as Adolphe says, " esteem, sooner or later, follows opulence." Secondly, it is significant in a negative way, because Constant did not represent Adolphe, after the disaster, as becoming a gambler, as he might so plausibly have done. If *Adolphe* were, in the sense so many critics assume, an autobiographical story, this is indeed what Constant would have done. But *Adolphe* is far more impressive than a strictly autobiographical story could ever be. It is the sudden and solitary utterance of the quintessence of Constant's experience in the form of an imaginative and dramatic parable. They are astray who seek, and think they have found, the original of Ellenore in Madame de Staël or Madame Lindsay or Madame this, that and the other, and still astray when they maintain she is a composite portrait drawn from them all. Ellenore is an authentic imaginative creation: a vision of woman surrendered to love. And the intensely dramatic conflict between Ellenore and Adolphe is something which Benjamin Constant never experienced in this life; he experienced only the adumbration of it. It is a conflict between principalities and powers, between potencies of the human soul, which never happened in that perfection and purity in the actual experience of Constant or any other man. It is a high spiritual drama which, in spite of its garment of realism, does not so much represent life as enable us to deepen our understanding of life.

And Adolphe himself is not so much drawn from Constant as drawn out of him. It is true he much more nearly represents Constant than Ellenore does the various women with whom Constant was at one time or other in love; but he represents a youthful Constant faced by the challenge of a woman such as he had never met, any more than Shakespeare had met a Desdemona, a Portia, or an Imogen. Even that formulation concedes too much to those who think they can explain a work of the creative imagination as autobiography. Adolphe is a potentiality of Constant's soul: a being whom he could convincingly imagine from the basis of his own familiar thoughts and feelings to be the spiritual antagonist of his imaginary and ideal woman. By the encounter Adolphe is killed as surely as Ellenore. But their deaths are of a different order. Ellenore is killed in the body, but her soul is triumphant. Adolphe lives in the body, but his soul is dead: or if it lives, it lives in and by the memory that an Ellenore once loved him, and loved him to the last.

Nothing of the kind happened to Benjamin Constant. He took to gambling. His soul never died. Whether it might have done had he met and killed an Ellenore is an idle speculation. We do not even know what really happened to Adolphe in his "posthumous existence." There is only the testimony of the imaginary person to whom the imaginary editor submitted the manuscript, that "he made no use of the liberty he reconquered at the cost of such tears and pain." The letters which this person is supposed to send to the editor to prove this remain disembodied, and the description of them is obviously intended more to indicate a view of Adolphe's character than to give information about his "actual" life. The only picture of him we have is that given by the editor when he met him in the Calabrian village. There, he is solitary, silent, and sad. One may say he *might* have been a gambler at other times. But this is wholly illegitimate. A character of fiction exists only in the words which actually describe him. When a character is the product of the true creative imagination, he takes on, indeed, a kind of independent existence in our imaginations, and we may wonder what "happened" to him outside the limits of the fiction itself. But this speculation is legitimate only in the form of wondering what his author may have imagined to be his subsequent fate. When we clearly understand this, it becomes evident that the author's imagination about him is confined to what he actually expressed. He may have had ideas about him; but these ideas, not having passed through the crucible of artistic expression, have no validity. This kind of "imagination," whether entertained by us or the author himself, is totally distinct from the creative imagination of the work of art. That alone has validity.

It follows that, if Adolphe, like Constant, had taken to gambling, Constant would have said so. The impression his author gives is that, after the death of Ellenore, Adolphe is a broken man. He is unable to live; he drags on a kind of " posthumous existence," to use once more the phrase of Keats describing his own life after he was parted for ever from Fanny Brawne. The cord that connected him to life is severed. And this is perfectly satisfying— not humanly, indeed, but as the fitting outcome of the spiritual drama in which alone Adolphe has his being.

The tension has become, at the moment where we left the story, intolerable. Adolphe has now become a monster of evil, not deliberately by an act of will, but by the weakness produced by the irremediable division of his being. The two parts of him which, while despising the Baron's world, cling to its values, in an access of fury against Ellenore, have acted. His egotism, stung by the Baron's contemptuous pity at Ellenore's claim upon him, has plunged him into a promise to tell her within three days that all is over. He cannot do it: but in his effort to gain more time, his egotism intervenes again. In his letter to the Baron he is prodigal of his assurances that he will do it. From now on the Baron may regard the liaison as over for ever.

Still he cannot tell her. Whether Adolphe surmises, or fears, the use the Baron may make of his letter is left in obscurity. What is not obscure is that Adolphe now feels certain of two things: that the end is at hand, and that *he* will not have to tell Ellenore. The end will come without his active agency. The two parts of him have abandoned Ellenore and sentenced her to death; the one part has drawn back. And because the one part has drawn back, because he will not tell Ellenore, he half-persuades himself that he has escaped responsibility. He has shifted it on to the nature of things, or destiny. And this astonishing self-deception, so far from seeming improbable and extravagant, appears to us entirely convincing. The Adolphe whom our normal vision plainly sees to be a monster, our imaginative sympathy declares to be a person whom at the least we must pity, and perhaps cannot refrain from loving. It is the only thing the better part in us can do.

So it is even with that last refinement of sensation or emotion which he now enjoys. "Enjoys" is too cruel a word. It is an intensity of feeling for which he has paid a heavy price, and will pay a heavier one.

> I looked on Ellenore as on a being I was going to lose. Her exigence, which had so often seemed intolerable, no longer frightened me. I felt my freedom in advance. In giving way to

her now I felt freer; and I experienced no more of the inward rebellion which in the past incessantly impelled me to tear everything to pieces. There was no more impatience in me; on the contrary, there was a secret desire to put off the fatal moment.

Ellenore noticed this increase of affection and tenderness, and became less bitter. Now I sought the conversations I had avoided: now I took delight in her words of love, which had irritated me before: now they were precious; each one of them might be the last.

It awakens an echo, and recalls the temper of Keats's *Ode on Melancholy*.

> She dwells with Beauty—Beauty that must die;
>   And Joy, whose hand is ever at his lips
> Bidding adieu; and aching Pleasure nigh.
>   Turning to poison while the bee-mouth sips:

But the dreadful difference is that the vision of Keats is indeed of a necessity in the nature of things. The poet has done nothing to speed on the death of Beauty or the passing of Joy. It is not his hand that puts the poison into the nectar-cup of Pleasure. It is there; and though the creatures of the moment forget it, it is ever-present to the imagination of the poet, who accepts the necessity, though his human heart rebels. It is the poet's privilege, the recompense for his pain, that he can discern and adore the sadness of beauty.

> Ay, in the very temple of Delight
>   Veil'd Melancholy has her sovran shrine,
>     Though seen of none save him whose strenuous tongue
> Can burst Joy's grape against his palate fine;
>   His soul shall taste the sadness of her might,
>     And be among her cloudy trophies hung.

But Adolphe is not only the piteous spectator of Beauty's death; he is the executioner himself. The part of him that can repudiate responsibility is infinitesimal. Yet it is enough to save him from being, in the eyes of imagination, the ghoul he is to sublunary vision. He too is a victim, it seems: his deathly philosophy has ended by making him the agent of Death.

So it is that, in spite of ourselves, we see Adolphe almost on a parity with Ellenore. She is his victim indeed; but they are victims both —of that philosophy of death which kills, before its time, the growth of life and love. Before its time. That is the operative phrase. It is man's duty to keep death in his place. Not by turning away from but by confronting him, and winning the victory over him: and the consequence of victory is that he is kept in his place: the servant, not the arbiter of life; the servant, not the equal, of God.

Constant now stretches the tragic irony to breaking-point.

One evening we parted after a conversation sweeter than usual. The secret I kept in my bosom saddened me; but my sadness was calm. The uncertainty in which I had contrived to wrap the time of our separation served to keep the idea of it away. During the night I heard an unfamiliar noise in the château. It was soon over, and I thought no more about it. But in the morning I remembered it, and wanted to know the cause. I went towards Ellenore's room. I was astounded to be told that for the last twelve hours she had

236

been in a burning fever, that a doctor summoned by her household said her life was in danger, and that she had given the strictest orders that I was not to be told or allowed to see her.

The Baron had sent Ellenore Adolphe's letter. Adolphe calls him cruel. But he had only done what the two parts of Adolphe desired, and the specious whole of him had sworn, to do. Now, faced by the terrible consequence of his act, in the fever and delirium of mortal sickness of Ellenore, he seeks to blot out his own words.

> "Weak, tortured, I may have yielded for a moment to a cruel pressure; but have you not yourself a thousand proofs that I cannot will our separation?"

The suggestion that he had yielded to pressure from the outside is false. Neither the Baron nor his father had brought any pressure to bear. True, his father had never concealed his disapproval of his liaison as soon as it became an impediment to the career he had planned for his son, and had asked the Baron to do what he could to detach him from Ellenore. But Constant deliberately depicts him as not doing what many fathers would have done, namely, to bring financial pressure to bear. And the Baron's influence is not pressure: it is only temptation. He has no influence at all beyond what Adolphe permits him to have. It is Adolphe himself who has projected his own ambitions into the figure of a menacing father, and with this figure he has threatened Ellenore.

"Let us begin a new life to-day," he cries. She looks at him doubtfully, with a faint flicker of hope.

> "Your father," she said at last. "Your duty, your family—what is expected of you. . . ."
> "Sometime, I suppose," I replied. "One day perhaps. . . ."
> She noticed my hesitation. "My God!" she cried, "why did he give me back hope only to snatch it away again?"

Again, ambiguity. What was it that Adolphe hesitated to say? It might have been that one day his father would be reconciled to his devotion to Ellenore; it might have been that one day their new life would also end, and he be free to fulfil his "duty." But the hesitation itself is now mortal to Ellenore. The last flicker of hope of happiness in this world with Adolphe dies as it was born.

Instantly, Ellenore is resigned. She might cry, like Cleopatra:

> My resolution's placed, and I have nothing
> Of woman in me: now, from head to foot,
> I am marble-constant; now the fleeting moon
> No planet is of mine.

The fluctuations of the troubled, longing, passionate soul have ceased. She is no longer a loving woman, but Love itself. There is not a trace of irony in the words with which her marvellous dialogue begins. She is all compassion and love.

" Adolphe, I thank you for your efforts. They have done me good—the more good because they will not cost you any sacrifice, I hope. But I beg of you, let us speak no more of the future.... Do not reproach yourself with anything, whatever happens. You have been good to me. I wanted the impossible. Love was all my life: it could not be all yours. Take care of me a few days longer."

Tears poured from her eyes; she breathed a little more freely; she leaned her head on my shoulder.

" Here," she said, " I always wanted to die."

I pressed her to my heart; again I abjured my plans, and disavowed my cruel angers.

" No," she said, " you must be free and contented."

" How can I be, if you are unhappy?"

" I shall not be unhappy long; you will not have long to be sorry for me."

I thrust away the fears that I wanted to believe imaginary.

" No, no, dear Adolphe," she said. " When we have cried for death a long while, heaven sends us at last a sure presentiment that our prayer is granted."

I swore to her that I would never leave her.

" I always hoped it, now I am certain of it."

It was one of those winter days when the sun sadly lights the grey countryside as though he looked with pity on the earth he has ceased to warm. Ellenore proposed that we should go out.

" It is very cold," I said.

" No matter, I want to go for a walk with you."

She took my arm; we walked for a long time in silence; she moved forward with difficulty, leaning nearly all her weight on me.

" Let us stop for a moment."

" No," she answered, " I love to feel myself still supported by you."

We were silent again. The sky was serene, but the trees were leafless. Not a breath moved

the air, not a bird flew through it.   Everything
was motionless; and the only sound was the crunching of the frozen grass under our feet.

"How calm everything is!" Ellenore said to
me.   "How nature is resigned!   Ought not the
heart also learn to be resigned?"

She sat down on a stone; suddenly she sank
on to her knees and bent her head, leaning it on
her two hands.   I heard her murmur some words.
I saw she was praying.   At last she got up.   "Let
us go back," she said.   "The cold has caught me.
I am afraid I may be ill.   Do not say anything to
me; I am not in a state to understand."

It is unbearably moving.

# CHAPTER VIII

Certain critics take it for granted that Ellenore was consumptive. They baldly assert the fact as though it were common knowledge. Their unfounded assurance indicates a misconception of the story. Apart from the fact that Constant gives no hint at all of this, and says quite explicitly that the doctors could discover no cause, the fable requires that Ellenore should die, not from any physical pre-disposition, but simply and solely through the unbearable tension created in her by Adolphe's divided being. Her surrender to love makes her utterly sensitive to him. The alternations of his love and his hate, his pity and his coldness, keep a condition of such endless inward agitation that her physical strength is consumed. Whether or not this is a disease known to the science of medicine is irrelevant. This is what Constant represents as happening; and the Ellenore he sets before our imagination is a woman to whom it could happen. We are entirely convinced that it does. Adolphe destroys Ellenore.

Though I know no reason why this could not happen in actual life, it would not diminish the power and impressiveness of the story one jot, if medical science were to be categorical in denying that it could. The import of the drama is not on that plane. It is a contest of souls; and the outcome of it is that the loving soul is liberated, and the faithless soul is enslaved.

Enslaved, and yet redeemed. Ellenore's love for Adolphe at the last, when she has resigned herself completely to death and made her simple peace with God, is such that it absolves him in our eyes. " One sentiment was unchanging in Ellenore's heart: her tenderness for me." When her physical strength is nearly all spent, she lavishes what remains of it in an effort to find in her box of papers the letter she had written for Adolphe to read after her death. She faints twice in the search for it. Unable herself to do what she desires to do—namely destroy it, she exacts a promise from him that he will destroy it unread. When he gives his promise, she is content. Her sole concern is that he shall not suffer, even from the truth.

The power of the perfection of this love of Ellenore for Adolphe is to our imagination like the grace of God. It works its simple miracle without his knowledge. He, on the human plane, is pierced to the heart by sorrow. Suddenly, now that Ellenore's love is to be taken from him, he realises what it has been. Ignorant, rebellious, cruel, he has nevertheless lived in an atmosphere of love. As she approaches death and the possibility of speech between them fades swiftly away, the atmosphere is withdrawn from him; and he knows what he has lost.

My pain was dull and solitary; I had no hope
of dying with Ellenore; I was to live without her
in this desert of the world, which I had so often
longed to travel through alone. I had broken the
heart which loved me, my own heart's mate, the
heart which had persisted in devotion to me, in
indefatigable tenderness. Isolation gripped me
already. Ellenore was still breathing, but I could
no longer confide my thoughts to her. I was
already alone on the earth, I lived no more in that
atmosphere of love which she spread around me;
the air I breathed seemed harsher, the faces I met
more indifferent. All nature seemed to be saying
to me that I was going to cease to be loved—for
ever.

Again, after Ellenore is dead, and the
moment in which he stares in uncomprehending
astonishment at her lifeless body is over:

I felt the last bond break, and the frightful
reality interpose for ever between her and me . . .
I was free, indeed; I was no longer loved; I was
a stranger to all the world.

But we, by the power of the artist's
imagination, see with other eyes into another
dimension. There by its own perfection the
love of Ellenore endures. It wraps Adolphe
round, though he is unconscious of it, and may
be for ever. It does not and cannot comfort
him; but it validates him. He was, and is
eternally, the cause and object of this love.

By a master-stroke of art this sense of the
two dimensions is concentrated and prolonged,
when Adolphe discovers and reads the letter
which he has promised to destroy unread. In
one dimension the letter has been obliterated.
If it contained the truth, it was only the partial

truth of the lower dimension. Ellenore's love
has disowned and destroyed it, as a cry torn
from her by her suffering, and therefore false
to love. But in the lower dimension it exists,
and Adolphe reads it. For him, and for us at
that moment, it is the bitter and scalding truth.
Nevertheless, it has been obliterated by love.
And this simultaneity of the existence and
non-existence of Ellenore's condemnation of
Adolphe makes, with entire simplicity, the impression that the truth of the lower dimension
is transcended by the truth of the higher.
Transcended, but not nullified. For in the
world of existence, Adolphe must now endure
the loneliness he has created about himself. His
unfriended wandering through the desert of
the world must continue. It is his punishment
and his purgatory. The last sentence of
Ellenore's letter is a sentence indeed.

> "And perhaps one day, when you are wounded
> by these unfeeling hearts, you will regret the
> heart of which you were the lord, which lived on
> your affection, which would have braved every
> danger to defend you, and which you no longer
> deign to reward with a look."

It is not "perhaps," and it is not in the
future. At the moment of Ellenore's death,
Adolphe realises it once for all. Then, for the
first time, he truly loves Ellenore. So long as
there is a gleam of hope for her life in this
world, he hesitates to make a full commitment
of himself. By that final hesitation, her death
is made certain, their separation irrevocable.

Then, and not till then, is he fully aware of her love; then and not till then does he fully respond to it. When for the first time there is nothing he can do to keep their love alive in the world of existence, then he surrenders to it.

It is very simple and very subtle. The overtones are such that they awaken thoughts beyond the reaches of our souls. Whether the effect was intentional or not, the final act of Adolphe recalls the final act of the central tragedy of Christianity. Adolphe is a thrice-denying Peter, who goes out and weeps bitterly, when he can no more do anything to help his Lord. So long as he could help him, he denied him. And I confess that it has even crossed my mind that there is a connection between the three days within which Adolphe promises the Baron that he will tell Ellenore that it is the end, and the three days of the Gospel story. For there is a mystery about Adolphe's three days. At the end of Chapter IX, Adolphe says: " Of the three days I had fixed, the second had nearly gone." But the narrative, as it was printed, contains no record of his having fixed a period of three days. Therefore, to mend the story, M. Gustav Rudler, the great authority on Benjamin Constant, has proposed that the words in brackets should be added to Adolphe's final words to the Baron.

" Yes," I cried. " I will give you my promise to break with Ellenore. [I will fulfil it in three days.] I will tell her myself. You can write to tell my father now."

The addition is, in a sense, necessary: the desire to make it very intelligible. Yet I can hardly believe that its omission was a mere oversight on Constant's part. I am more inclined to believe that he shrank from certain associations aroused in his mind by the open declaration: "I will fulfil it in three days." He, or the genius within the man of genius, preferred to leave it in penumbra.

This notion of mine, I admit, may be merely fanciful; but it is intimately connected with the strong sense I have of an affinity between the tragedy of *Adolphe* and the central Christian tragedy. For that I cannot apologise. The more I try to penetrate the significance of *Adolphe*, the more strongly I feel this affinity, so that I would finally describe it as a re-statement of the Christian tragedy and the Christian revelation by a man for whom orthodox Christianity no longer possessed objective truth, but who retained a Christian sensibility and who was at heart a profoundly religious man.

I am not arguing that Constant consciously intended *Adolphe* to be such a re-statement. The resemblance or affinity may have "happened." But it happened by a real necessity in the nature of things. The quality of life does not change; and the sensitive soul who broods upon it finds himself staring at the same eternal question: What is the significance of love and death? Which of these two powers has dominion over the other? Christianity is an answer to this question; and so is *Adolphe*. And the answers are essentially the same: namely, that love has dominion over death. And in both cases this answer is revealed. Orthodox Christianity of course does more than that. It is, so to speak, not content with what is revealed in the tragedy of the man of love. It asserts the triumph of love that is revealed as a reality in the higher dimension as a fact in the lower dimension. The victory of Jesus is that on the third day he rose again from the dead in his physical body. That is the corner-stone of the orthodox Christian faith. To me—and I must put my cards on the table—this is a confusion of the two dimensions. I call myself, and believe I am, a Christian; but I have never experienced any desire or need or compulsion to believe in the physical resurrection of Jesus. His eternal existence is simply and finally revealed to me in the tragedy of the Cross, and in the direct assurance given in contemplation of the tragedy that it is not a defeat but a victory of love. Perfect love is triumphant over death. " O death where is thy sting? O grave, where is thy victory?"

In *Adolphe* I receive essentially the same

revelation. It seems to make no difference that whereas I am certain that the life of love and the cruel death of Jesus were historical facts, in *Adolphe* I know from the beginning that Ellenore is a creature of the imagination: created by the imagination of one Benjamin Constant, and re-created in my own. That seems to make no difference: for, although I verily believe that Jesus lived and taught and was betrayed on this earth and was " crucified under Pontius Pilate," it is only in virtue of the imagination in me that these things are real to me. In other words, it is in the world of imagination that Jesus is real, and in that world alone is he real. In that same world of imagination Ellenore is also real. That is not to say, or imply, that the character of fiction is of the same order as the person who, I am persuaded, really lived on this earth. In the world of imagination, in which they are both real, there is no difficulty whatever in holding to the distinction between a historical person and an imaginary one. And for aught I know the distinction may be of the utmost importance.

But I have to confess that at the moment the distinction does not seem very important to me: for my difficulty is to prevent the created character of fiction from becoming as real as the historical person. I have incessantly to remind myself that an Ellenore did not really exist. I have to tug continually at

the sleeve of my imagination, and say to it,
" But these are the creations of a human mind."
But even when I have said it, and by force of
repetition compelled my imagination to listen,
I am by no means sure that it makes any sig-
nificant difference.

For I am by no means sure that, when I
apply the phrase, " creations of the human
mind" to the figures of a drama which
" reveals " what I have called the higher dimension, I have said anything meaningful.    The
creations of the human mind are innumerable;
but few of them indeed have this quality of
revelation.    Moreover, I am inclined to doubt
whether it can be deliberately and consciously
achieved.    Certainly, in the particular case of
*Adolphe*, I do not think it was deliberately
achieved.    If we like the phrase, we may say
that Constant's " unconscious " took control.
That does not seem to me an improvement on
the old word " inspiration."    And the question
that arises is whether these rare creations of
the human mind do not owe their peculiar and
precious quality of revelation to the fact that
the human mind gives way to, or is dis-
possessed by, a super-human mind.    There is
an immemorial tradition which affirms this;
and so did Coleridge who was a great critic,
and at moments a great poet, too.

None of the words we use to describe this
fact, or this possibility, are very satisfactory.
The super-human mind, the divine mind—they

seem to beg a great question.   And perhaps
the problem is, by its very nature, unformul-
able, because it falls within the scope of the
dictum: "What can be revealed cannot be
uttered."   But finally it all comes back to the
question of the *reality* of the revelation of love
as triumphant over death.   I do not think it
would be difficult to show that all those great
"creations of the human mind" with which
we are here concerned are great, precisely
because they do in many different ways and
degrees give the impression of making this
revelation.   It is open, I suppose, to anybody
to say that this revelation is an illusion.   That
attitude is impossible to me; and it is certain
that it begs the question much more seriously
and hopelessly than the attitude which seeks
the explanation of the experience in the working of a super-human or divine mind.  For the
experience itself is not illusory.   To those who
experience it there *is* revelation.   But of what
is there revelation?   The simple traditional
answer is: God, who is love.   And that is
satisfying to me.   If, for some cause and on
some occasion, I am chary of using the word,
I may say it is a revelation of a higher dimension, a higher order of reality; but, without a
context, this does not indicate the distinctive
and peculiar quality of the experience: namely,
that it is a revelation and experience of love.

This I think is true of the experience in all
its forms.   The work of the poet, the painter,

the prophet is truly and permanently significant only in so far as it expresses and communi-
cates the vision of love, which is " self-destroying."   This inward tendency of art to express
the vision of love reaches its highest pitch in
tragedy, of which the essence is that it shall
reveal the nobility of the human spirit as un-
annihilable by circumstance, or even by its own
weakness and error.   Even when the nobility
of the tragic hero is not conspicuously the
nobility of love, but is manifest as a striving
after some goal we recognise as good, the impression left upon us is that this nobility is not
wasted, still less annihilated; and the impression immediately passes into another, namely,
that the power which orders this enduringness
or eternality of the nobility of the noble soul
is a power of love.   And this tendency of
tragedy, in turn, reaches its highest pitch, when
the tragic hero is animated to an extreme
degree by the power of love.

The archetype of this culmination of
tragedy is the life and death of Jesus.  The man
who was convinced of the reality of the God of
love, and devoted his life to teaching that faith
and doctrine to unhappy men, was put to a
cruel death for doing so; and in his suffering
and his disaster the truth of his doctrine is
revealed, perhaps an even deeper truth than he
knew.  That is the incontrovertible basis of the
Christian religion.  So far I believe it to be

based upon historical fact; but I also believe that the assertion that he rose in his physical body from the grave is not historical fact at all, but an endeavour to assert in terms of existence the truth of another and higher order, namely that in Jesus is revealed the victory of love over death. I make no doubt that, without that transfer of spiritual truth to the order of physical fact, whereby the spiritual becomes the miraculous, the Christian religion would never have attained the universality which it did attain. But it seems to me that mankind has now reached a point where it can and therefore eventually must dispense with the aid of the miraculous in its effort to realise the spiritual. The revelation of the God who is love is made completely in the story of the life and death of Jesus: the legend of his physical resurrection adds nothing to it. The love that is awakened in our souls by the tragedy of Jesus is *itself* the assurance of his victory, the evidence of the God who is love.

I would go further still in my heresy, and suggest that even in the minds of those who firmly believe in the physical resurrection of Jesus, he is resurrected in reality only in the world of imagination; and that nothing else is possible. The Jesus who is resurrected in the physical body must of necessity at this point of time be a figure of, or in, the imagination. The belief that he was a physical reality in the experience of certain men and women of two thousand years ago does not alter this fundamental incapacity of the human mind to-day to conceive him save by and in the imagination.

I use the word imagination in a sense totally distinct from fantasy. Imagination is the condition into which the mind enters when it is possessed by the power of love: it is the condition meant by William Blake when he said: "Imagination is the Human existence itself." It is a new dimension of experience which is self-evidently higher than any ordinary mode of experience. It is the medium of revelation, and is itself revelation. Historically, for men of the West anyhow, the contemplation of the life and death of Jesus has been the chief means by which they have gained access to the world of imagination, and by which the power of imagination has been developed in them. For he is at once the supremely imaginative man, and his apparent disaster the supreme test of the validity of the imagination.

Thus it is natural to regard Jesus—if we may use a metaphor—as the Lord of the realm of imagination; or, using the more mystical language of Blake, to say that the Imagination is comprehended in " the Divine Humanity, the one Man, even Jesus." Wherever the imagination takes possession, there is manifest the same power of love which was revealed in Jesus.

I assume, as self-evident, that the imagination took possession of Constant when, in a fortnight, he wrote *Adolphe*. It is, to me, plainly an inspired piece of writing. It has that quality intrinsically; and as the solitary utterance in fiction of a man whose most serious and sustained thinking was devoted to the problem of religion, of which *Adolphe* is an epitome, we might expect, or at least hope, that it would be quintessential. The theme on which imagination worked in him was the struggle between a woman wholly surrendered to love and a man of his own subtle and divided nature. What that nature was I have already described. But, once again, he was a man in whom mind and heart were in irreconcilable conflict. The mind in him was dominant. From early youth it had become convinced that death was " the end of all." Too acute and sensitive to acquiesce in the dull indifference of men towards the problem of death, or to be reconciled to the animal unconsciousness which pursues the values of this world with unthinking conviction and regards death as unreal, he perpetually anticipated death. It was the starting point of his philosophy. In this attitude he was more genuinely religious than the majority of religious people: for although the professed Christian is saved by his faith from being oppressed by the finality of death, he is saved from it only on condition that, instead of anticipating death, he anticipates the Judgment; and that he seldom does.

In fact he frequently behaves as though it was the easiest thing in the world at once to believe in God and cheat him. For Adolphe death was real, if God was not; and that is a good deal more religious than the specious religion which treats both death and God as unreal.

Adolphe, deeply convinced of the finality of death, is therefore convinced that the values of this world are ephemeral and illusory. He cannot pursue them with ardour or conviction. This fundamental indifference to the values of this world sets him apart and makes him lonely, so that he is beset by a craving for the experience of a woman's love, the companionship of the understanding soul, the communion of the surrendered body. But, while he craves for love, he is persuaded that it must, by the nature of things, be a transient experience. It must be as ephemeral as the flux of existence from which it seems to offer a momentary escape. It is the opportunity of a fleeting rapture, a sweet intoxication, in the midst of which the conscious man will never forget that it is doomed to die. In other words, Adolphe seeks love as a man in pain would seek a narcotic, or a bored man the intoxication of alcohol.

But in Ellenore he meets a woman to whom this attitude is entirely alien: a woman to whom love is, by its own nature an eternal bond, and who looks with abhorrence upon a liaison into which a man and woman enter with the knowledge that it cannot and the determination that it shall not last. This very quality in Ellenore, which Adolphe senses, attracts him irresistibly. She offers, if he can win her, an experience of love far rarer than anything he has imagined; but with this hope is mingled a baser desire, belonging to the world he affects to despise, and springing from the vanity which seeks its esteem—namely, the desire for a notable conquest.

Ellenore, on her side, is sensitive to this turmoil of jarring elements within him. Perhaps, if she could clearly distinguish them, she would draw back. But she is conscious only of his total agitation and unhappiness. The compassion which this excites in her makes him more eager to win her and the intimacy of her sympathetic soul, and the more desperate at the thought of failure. He appears to manifest " the very ecstasy of love." Part of Ellenore is deceived, as Adolphe is himself deceived, by his suffering and has compassion on an Adolphe who does not exist; but another part of her makes no mistake. This part is responsive to the potentiality of love in him, the authenticity of his longing to be released from the prison of his own self. So that Ellenore, while not yet knowing what he is, yet loves him for what he is. To this love she surrenders. At the moment of her surrender she hopes and believes that the power of love in her will heal this division and make him

happy. Though this belief is vain and the
hope is dashed to pieces on Adolphe's incapacity to surrender himself to love, her love endures. It is purified and ennobled by the
agonies she suffers. As the woman in her comes
to fear him as a relentless destroyer of her life,
so the love in her forgives him and is, bit by bit
and drop by drop, reconciled to her destiny.
She sees, by the vision of love, that she must
be killed. The price of being faithful to her
love is death. To escape it, she must cease to
love him, since he cannot be changed. And
she cannot cease to love him. She pays the
price, though the woman in her rebels so long
as there is a gleam of hope of life and love
together. At last she passes through her
Gethsemane, and she is irradiated and trans-
figured by the utter purity of her love.

On Adolphe's side, only her death can
break through the veil of his unawareness of
her. Only when he sees that it is inevitable,
does the doubtful knowledge that he is going
" to be ceased to be loved for ever " flash upon
him. The condition of being loved by Ellenore,
which in his selfish self-absorption he had come
to feel as an intolerable limitation on his freedom, he now suddenly sees to be the only condition in which he could be free: for the only
freedom mortals know is the freedom which
love creates. Constant puts Adolphe's realisation in the simple and profound words, with
which he concludes the story of Ellenore's

death: "I was free, indeed; I was no longer loved; I was a stranger to all the world."

The parable of the tragedy is profound. I make no apology for comparing it with the central tragedy of Christianity, because I believe that in writing *Adolphe* Constant was possessed by the imagination and inspired by the love of which the life and death of Jesus reveals to us the reality. It is the work of a Christian sensibility which has parted from Christian orthodoxy, and yet has achieved, or in a moment of inspiration is uplifted to, a vision indistinguishable from that of the Christian revelation itself. From this point of view we may say that the character of Adolphe himself represents the Christian sensibility which has lost the capacity of understanding that love supersedes the knowledge of the intellect, and is itself the highest mode of knowledge.

This conviction of the metaphysical status and validity of love is the inestimable gift of Christianity to mankind. Because Adolphe is incapable of it, his Christian sensibility is only a sensibility: it is purely emotional, and its momentary compulsiveness is resented and despised by his intellectual part, which however cannot eradicate it. The separation of sensibility from faith issues in a kind of morbid perversity of behaviour, whereby the intellectual man tortures the heart of the loving woman, while the emotional man cannot detach himself from her pain: so that Adolphe appears to nourish his soul on the suffering he causes. One understands why so many contemporary readers of the story found his character "revolting." Equally, one understands why the verdict has not been sustained by posterity. For there is more to Adolphe than this. The truth that there is more is conveyed to our imagination, simply and directly, by the fact that Ellenore never falters in her love of him; and this love of hers never appears to be the tenacious animal affection which women sometimes feel for a worthless man. It is conveyed to us also by the fact that Adolphe, to the utmost of his capacity, is changed by the love which radiates through Ellenore's unresisting final surrender of herself to death. To say that by it he is converted to love would be to say too much; but at least he comes to understand that love is not "an intoxication of the senses," but a supernatural power which can transfigure life. He understands that the kingdom of heaven has been about him, and that by the blindness of his egotism he has been unaware of it. He has been like the man who came to the wedding-feast without a wedding-garment.

He knows it. In one sense, he does not have to wait for the sentence of expulsion. He knows that he is expelled, and that he has expelled himself. But he also knows from what he has been expelled, and he did not know that before; and he knows that in spite of all he has been forgiven and loved. The angel of love has torn up the indictment. But what he does not know is whether that was the act of a particular loving woman, or the act of the universal power of love as well. Has it been just one touching and pathetic instance of devotion in a world of transient and unmeaning experience of which death is the final end, or has it been a gesture of veritable absolution? Has he been forgiven and loved by Ellenore, or by God? We see and know that these are the same. Perhaps Adolphe never does.

But the cause why we see and know it lies in the power and purity of Constant's imagination. For all we know, the actual quotidian Benjamin may never himself have been quite sure. If we could ask him: What do you *really* believe? he would perhaps have been unable to say. Perhaps he might have said " I am not entirely a real person, so what can I really believe?" Perhaps he would have pointed to *Adolphe* and said: " I believe what the man who wrote that believed." These replies would have been consistent with each other. For the " unreal being " of Benjamin Constant became real in the writing of *Adolphe*. For once an impersonal power informed his personality, and enabled him to reveal what cannot be uttered. And this is true both of the subject and the object. The seemingly contradictory elements of his personality, whose incessant conflict led him to describe himself as " not entirely a real person," were suddenly integrated in an act of complete expression; and this expression was complete because it was crystallized about an imagined conflict which embodied his deepest thoughts and feelings concerning the problem of existence. He revealed himself and the truth at the same moment, whereas neither could be uttered.

Utterance, in this sense, means assertion. When, in life, Benjamin Constant asserted, he was, like his friends, dismayed by the discrepancy between his acts and his words. His acts (like Adolphe's) were often generous and devoted, but his words seemed to belie them. So also, in the realm of religion, with which he was so deeply concerned, assertion seemed to make for falsity. " In irreligion," he wrote in his *Journal Intime*, " there is something vulgar and threadbare which is repugnant to me. I have my religion, but it is all in sentiments and emotions, which are often vague and cannot be reduced to a system." In *Adolphe* he asserts nothing. He is content to reveal.

# CHAPTER IX

A sort of dialectic concerning the import of *Adolphe* was carried on in Constant's own mind, which he expressed through the views of the imaginary Editor of the manuscript and the imaginary person to whom it was submitted, whom we may call the Critic. The Critic, after admitting that Adolphe was " a malign being " who tore Ellenore to pieces by his weakness, puts the blame for the catastrophe on society. He says the story proves " that the most passionate sentiment cannot struggle against the order of things," by which he plainly means the established social order. In fact, the Critic offers two explanations of the tragedy: one (on which he chiefly expatiates) is that society, under the pretext of morality, sets itself to destroy a love that is not " legitimate "; the other, that Adolphe was " punished by his qualities even more than his defects, because his qualities derived from his emotions and not from his principles." The two explanations are not inconsistent with each other. Indeed, they combine quite naturally into this: Adolphe's malign weakness lay in the fact that he had no principles on which to base a resistance to the destructive will of society. His good qualities were purely emotional, and had no basis or backing in principles.

The Editor, while not directly challenging

this, shifts the question of the meaning of the story on to a different level. "It is," he says, echoing Pascal, "a true story of the misery of the human heart." Its lesson is for men.

> It proves that the intellect they are so proud of, avails neither to find happiness nor to give it; it proves that character, strength, fidelity, goodness are gifts they must ask from heaven. . . . . The great problem of life is the suffering we cause, and the most ingenious metaphysic does not justify the man who has lacerated the heart which loved him.

We have already considered the ingenious metaphysic of Adolphe. It was a philosophy based on the finality of death. It became ingenious, or super-subtle, by the sleight of mind which transformed an honest if unjustifiable conviction that love was transient because death was the end of all, into a deliberate effort to make love transient. A bond which should have been recognised as enduring unto death, even if it could not endure beyond, was of set purpose trivialized and frayed. This, it may be argued, was only a consistent application of the philosophy itself. But, applied to a love-relation, from the beginning it involved deliberate deceit. If Adolphe had told Ellenore the truth of what he believed about life and love, she would have rejected him with indignation. Thus the inevitable consequence of this philosophy is that, if honestly declared, it excludes the man who maintains it from contact with natures which acknowledge transcendent obligations, or condemns him to deliberate dissimulation towards such natures. But why does he hold the original philosophy except in consequence of a felt obligation to acknowledge the truth? A philosophy which begins in obligation to truth and ends by repudiating it, has become corrupt on the journey. To save itself from this corruption, it must proclaim itself fearlessly, and face the consequence of excommunication by natures to which it is alien and revolting.

This is what Constant had in mind when he made a cryptic remark in the *Journal Intime*. " Integrity of mind (*la justesse d'esprit*) is impossible at certain periods except by heroic abnegation or complete degradation." The philosophy of death, seriously held, involves the repudiation of all values and the denial of all moral law. The man who holds it has two choices : either to hold himself rigorously aloof from all communion with men and women who recognise values and the moral law, or to degrade himself completely by behaving towards them in entire defiance of all law. It can be argued, as it was by some of Dostoevsky's antinomian " heroes," that the latter choice is the truly consistent one. But that is on the assumption that a man can be absolutely convinced of the truth of the philosophy of death. I hold that that is impossible. So did Constant, as we shall see. It can never appear more than probable to a mind of in-

tegrity that death is the end of all. Certainty
in this matter is unattainable by the nature of
things. If by pretending that a probability is
a certainty one were to be seduced into denying
the reality of obligation and the moral law,
the consequence would be inward chaos. For
again it can never be more than probable—if
indeed it can be that—that the sense of obligation is illusory. On the strength of a mere
hypothesis deliberately to deceive and inflict
suffering on others is sheer diabolism : the
suicide of the human spirit. There is no real
alternative to heroic abnegation in complete
degradation.

But as intellectual possibilities—afterwards imaginatively realised by Dostoevsky
in the characters of Kirillov and Svidrigailov—
they indicate the frame of reference within
which *Adolphe* was conceived. In thought Constant anticipated the *âmes damnées* of the
generation to follow; but Adolphe hardly
belongs to them. He would at least have
agreed with the imaginary Editor that " the
most ingenious metaphysic does not justify the
man who has lacerated the heart which loved
him."

In the Editor's next train of thought:
" Besides I detest the imbecility of a mind
which believes it has excused what it has explained " and the rest, I detect a subtle irony
of mystification. For in the story Adolphe
cea s to do this. There is no trace of self-

justification in the final chapter. Constant
must have known this perfectly well. Therefore his imaginary Editor does not fully understand the story.

Thus we have three levels or aspects of
understanding presented to us: the Critic's, the
Editor's, and a third, which is not so much
presented as implied by the fact that the other
two are inadequate, without being false. They
call for further examination.

tears Ellenore to pieces by his weakness. That
First, the Critic. He declares that Adolphe
is true. He then explains how this happened.
There is in society a blind will to destroy a
love which it does not sanction. Under the
disguise of morality those incapable of love
seek to destroy it. This also is true, because
those capable of love would, by that very
capacity, be restrained from seeking to destroy
it. To resist this will to the destruction of
love which emanates from society, a man needs
principles—that is, a philosophy in which he
firmly believes, and which will enable him to
remain faithful to his love in defiance of society.
It must therefore be a philosophy which holds
that love is a value superior to the values of
society. Adolphe had no such philosophy. He
had only emotions, and not principles.

In this sense we must read the Critic's
declaration that " Ellenore's disaster proves
that the most passionate sentiment cannot

266

struggle against the order of things." Something deeper than the most passionate sentiment is required, which Ellenore had and Adolphe had not. And that is implied by his previous statement that it was Adolphe's weakness that destroyed Ellenore.

It is not a superficial interpretation; it is coherent and penetrating.

The Editor takes *Adolphe* from another angle. He associates Adolphe's weakness with an ingenious and false metaphysic deriving from the intellect alone, which is impotent to find happiness or to give it. But he gives no indication of what he holds to be the true metaphysic. He says simply that " character, strength, fidelity, goodness are gifts we must ask from heaven." Whether he means this literally he does not make clear. Are they gifts for which we must pray to God, believing in his existence? Or does he use the phrase " gifts from heaven " in the current, trivial sense, of natural endowments? I think his meaning inclines definitely towards the former. Otherwise, there is little point in his declaring his detestation of " the vanity which . . . analyses itself instead of repenting." Again he says: " Circumstances count for little, character is everything; it is useless to break with things and persons, if you cannot break with yourself."

To judge by the language alone this " breaking with yourself," this " repentance,"

by which alone Adolphe could have achieved
" character "—in the sense in which it includes
" strength, fidelity, goodness "—are conceived
as Christianity conceives them.   " Make me a
clean heart, O God, and renew a right spirit
within me!"   But not in the sense of conventional Christianity.   In that case, the outcome
of Adolphe's repentance would be that he
should break off his " sinful " relation with
Ellenore: for the Editor it is that he should be
vouchsafed the character, strength, fidelity and
goodness to be faithful to her.

Thus the Critic and the Editor are at one
in taking it for granted that the consequence
of Adolphe's having " principles," in the one
analysis, and " character " in the other, is that
he would have been faithful to Ellenore.   The
Critic roundly declares that conventional
morality is the disguise under which " society
arms itself with all that is bad in a man's heart
to discourage all that is good in it."   " Principles " and " character " are what Adolphe
needed to be faithful to the good in himself,
which was the part of him that desired to be
faithful to Ellenore.

This valuation of love and loyalty to love
is in harmony with that which emerges from
the story itself.   Exposition can never be on
the same level as revelation; the utterance of
authentic imagination can never be fully trans-
lated.   It is enough that exposition should not

conflict with revelation; and neither of these
expositions do. On the contrary, they are in
harmony with it, because in their non-imagina-
tive language they too assume the necessity
and the reality of revelation. It is true that,
both being concerned with the character of
Adolphe alone, they imply the necessity and
reality of revelation only in regard to his
moral nature: his need of repentance, and of
the gifts from heaven that follow on repentance, if he was to have the " character " and
" principles " by virtue of which he would be
loyal to love. But they leave it in no doubt
that the purpose and outcome of the change
they desire in Adolphe is fidelity to love, as
manifest in Ellenore. That is to say, the
morality they inculcate is based on the conviction that love is the supreme good. To become
convinced of it is to acquire " principles " and
" character " and gain the strength to with-
stand the destructive power which society dis-
guises as conventional morality.

That, indubitably, is the doctrine of
*Adolphe*. The point at which the exposition
falls short of the story and, we may surmise,
short of the imaginative interpretation of Constant himself, is that in the story we are made
to feel that Adolphe himself participates in
the revelation of love in Ellenore's death. He
is not, indeed, fully illumined by it: for that
would issue in a conviction of the immortality
of love, and of the loving soul. Adolphe can-

not rise to this. But at least we are made to feel that his condemnation of himself at this point is absolute: there are no more egotistic reservations, he is purged of that subtler vanity which believes that in explaining it has excused itself. He trembles on the very brink of renewal and faith. That it does not come to him is, we feel, due (at least in part) to the very depth of his sense of guilt. He has killed Ellenore. He knows that Ellenore has forgiven him; but that, instead of lightening, increases his burden of guilt. He can understand, he can expound, but he cannot forgive himself.

Humanly, and divinely, speaking there is only one possibility of release for Adolphe: that he should be visited by the divine love, by the knowledge that he *is* forgiven. Then the revelation that brushed him with its wings in Ellenore's death would completely enfold him. He is, or he is represented to be, debarred from that. The unearthly pathos of the story is that while we, in virtue of the revelation of love, see that Adolphe is forgiven, and that Ellenore's forgiveness of him is God's, he himself cannot. In the simple gospel story, Judas who has betrayed Jesus to death, goes out and hangs himself. But Judas's crime was greater. And that is a drama of black and white, in which it is not possible to see into the mystery of Judas's consciousness. We can see into Adolphe's, and suicide is no answer. He lives

270

on, as it were in a kind of limbo, suspended between two worlds—the world of existence, to which Ellenore's love had made him an alien, and the world of love's eternity, to which he cannot attain.

There is a terrifying veracity in Constant's imagination—an immense and limpid subtlety, as though he were contemplating with a super-human detachment the drama of the contact of a nature like his own with the love of an ideal woman. The two contemporaneous "commentaries" on the narrative of the imaginary Adolphe which we have been con-sidering (it is perhaps unnecessary to insist) are an integral part of *Adolphe*. They belong to the same act of creation. They are more severe to Adolphe than Constant's imagination was; but they proclaim the doctrine of the story. They fulfil something of the function of a chorus in a Greek tragedy, and are in the same way consubstantial with it.

This, however, is not the case with the author's later preface (Préface de la Troisième Edition, 1824) which is generally printed with the story. This is neither contemporaneous nor consubstantial with it. It is interesting, of course, as anything which Constant wrote about *Adolphe* must be: but much of it comes from a different level. *Adolphe* was written in 1807. It was not published till 1816, but it had certainly achieved its final form in 1810.

271

It is not possible in the present state of our
knowledge, to say whether it underwent any
considerable alteration between 1807 and 1810.
But there is nothing in the external evidence
as yet available to conflict with my impression
that *Adolphe* as originally written in 1807 was
substantially the same as the book published
in 1816.

The preface of 1824 reveals a Constant
busy, characteristically enough, in covering
up his own tracks. If there is any fragment
of truth in his statement that it was written
" with the sole idea of convincing a few friends,
gathered in the country, that it was possible
to give a kind of interest to a novel with only
two characters, whose situation did not
change ": the fragment must be very small. In
any case it is unimportant. At best, it describes the occasion, not the cause, of *Adolphe*.
Constant himself goes on to say that, when he
had begun, " other ideas supervened, which
seemed to have a certain usefulness."

I wished to depict the harm done even to
arid hearts by the sufferings they cause to others,
and the illusion which induces them to believe
themselves more immoral and corrupt than they
really are. At a distance, the pain men inflict
appears vague and confused, like a cloud through
which one can easily pass; they are encouraged
by the approval of a thoroughly artificial society
which has rules instead of principles and conventions instead of emotions, and which hates
scandal because it is troublesome, not because it
is immoral, for it welcomes vice when there is no

scandal attached to it; they think that attachments formed without reflection can be broken without trouble. But when they see the anguish caused by breaking these attachments; the astonishment and pain of a soul deceived, the mistrust which follows complete trust, and which, directed against the being who stood higher than the rest of the world, extends itself to the whole world; the desire to esteem thrust back upon itself and knowing nowhere to fasten;—then they realise that there is something sacred in the heart which suffers because it loves, and they discover how deep are the roots of the affection which they thought to inspire without feeling it themselves, and if they overcome what is called weakness, it is by destroying in themselves all generosity, loyalty, nobility and goodness. They emerge from this victory, which friends and the indignant applaud, having killed a portion of their soul, set sympathy at defiance, taken advantage of weakness, outraged morality by using it as a pretext for cruelty, and, ashamed or degraded by this miserable success, they live on while their better nature is dead.

That was what I tried to depict in *Adolphe*. I do not know if I have succeeded; what makes me feel that it possesses at least the merit of a certain veracity, is that nearly all the readers I have met have spoken of themselves as having been in the situation of my hero. It is true that through the regrets they expressed at all the pain they had caused one felt a kind of satisfied self-complacency. They liked to depict themselves as having been, like Adolphe, pursued by the obstinate affection they have inspired, and victims of the immense love conceived for them. I believe that for the most part they calumniated themselves, and that, if their vanity had left them undisturbed, their conscience could have been at peace.

All that is serious enough. It is another angle on *Adolphe*. But Constant ends as he began with the affectation that it is a trifle. All that concerns *Adolphe* has, he says, become a matter of complete indifference to him; he attaches no value to it; and his only reason for republishing it is to declare that this is the only authentic text. Those statements can be reconciled with one another if we suppose that Constant was offered some ready money for the right to publish a third edition of Adolphe with his public *imprimatur*: which is probable in itself, for it seems that what decided him to publish the original edition of 1816 was the offer of £70 by Colburn, the London publisher. But this insouciance towards publication does not indicate his attitude towards the story itself. He frequently read it to intimate and appreciative circles during the nine years which elapsed between writing and publishing it. He wrote in a letter: " I only published it to save myself from having to read it. After reading it four times in one week, I thought it better that others should take the trouble to read it themselves." That does not square at all with his statement that he set no value on it. Indeed, the statement is intrinsically incredible. We may conclude that the first and last paragraphs of the preface of 1824 are a gentlemanly mystification.

The substance of it, which I have quoted, is much more valuable. There is the same condemnation of polite society as " entirely

artificial," as was made by the Critic and Editor
in the story itself. Society substitutes rules
for principles, and conventions for emotions.
This connects directly with the Critic's diag-
nosis of Adolphe as a man whose qualities had
their root in his " emotions and not in his principles." Adolphe is thus set midway between
a conforming member of the artificial society
who has neither genuine principles nor genuine
emotions, and the good man whose genuine
emotions are strengthened by genuine principles. It is a just schematic way of "placing"
Adolphe, provided we remember that the harmony of emotions and principles in the good
man is achieved by a philosophy or religion
which recognises that love is the supreme value.

In Adolphe, according to this scheme, the
vacuum which principles should occupy is filled
by " rules." They are not believed in, because
they conflict with the emotions which are
genuine, but in default of principles to
strengthen and purify the emotions the rules
are allowed to decide action. The true situation is more fully revealed by the part played
in *Adolphe* by the Baron than it is expressed
by this formal analysis; but the formal analysis is useful. By thus submitting his action
in a love-relation to the rules of conventional
society, a sensitive man inflicts suffering. But
then he comes to realise that " there is something sacred in the heart which suffers because
it loves." This moment is crucial. It is the

opportunity of worshipping the sacred thing that is revealed, of repenting the wrong one has done, and of becoming the servant of love. This is not said in so many words, but is clearly implied in Constant's language. His picture is of even arid hearts suffering from the sufferings they inflict, and forced by them to discard the illusion that they are more insensitive and corrupt than they really are. In the suffering of a loving woman they have a glimpse of the holiness of love. The glimpse may become a decisive revelation, and then they are saved. But " if they overcome what is called weakness "—in other words, harden their souls to the revelation—then they do so by destroying in themselves " generosity, loyalty, nobility and goodness." Their better nature is killed, and they live on.

This is, in the highest degree, pertinent to the story. It is true and subtle psychology expressed with a simplicity of which the overtones and implications may easily escape unalert readers. He characteristically puts them off the scent by inserting it between two pieces of gentlemanly mystification. Again, the only point at which this psychological analysis falls short of the actual impression made by *Adolphe* is that it does not allow for the fact that the revelation of the sacredness of suffering love comes to Adolphe at the moment of Ellenore's death. Nothing in the analysis is inconsistent with this possibility. Adolphe is one who

276

tries to harden his soul against the glimpse of
the sacred in Ellenore's suffering; but at the
last, when it is too late and the response can
do nothing to save her, he does respond. By
that intensification the psychological process
which Constant describes is lifted into the
realm of high tragedy. One might say the
realm of the Christian revelation, were it not
that Adolphe's illumination cannot rise beyond
remorse. But it would not be true simply to
say of him that he " survives his better nature."
It is not killed, but it is stunted because it cannot expand into religious faith.

Much of the matter in the valuable part
of this preface of 1824 was contained in a preface which Constant wrote in 1816 and published in the second edition of that year. It
was discovered and published by M. Gustav
Rudler in 1935. This earlier preface contains
a first version of the important psychological
analysis we have just been discussing; but it
contains other things, among them a vehement
protest against those who identified his characters with actual persons. It was unavailing,
for critics have never ceased to do so. But the
right is on Constant's side.

> This mania for recognising in works of
> imagination individuals whom one meets in society
> is for the works themselves a perfect scourge. It
> degrades them, gives them a false tendency,
> destroys their interest and annihilates their useful-
> ness.

That has been eminently the case with *Adolphe*; but, important though the statement is, it is less important than the following passage.

> Some people have asked me what Adolphe should have done to suffer less and cause less suffering. His position and that of Ellenore were hopeless, and that was exactly what I intended. I have shown him tormented because his love for Ellenore was feeble; but he would have been not less tormented if he had loved her more. He suffered through her, for lack of feeling; with a more passionate feeling, he would have suffered for her. Society, disapproving and disdainful, would have poured all its poisons into an affection which it had not sanctioned.
>
> Not to begin such liaisons is what is wanted for happiness in life: when one has entered on that road, there is only a choice of evils.

So much was printed as the final paragraph of the preface to the second edition of 1816. But there has survived a draft which sets this judgment in perspective. Significantly it omits the last sentence and continues:

> That is what I wanted to demonstrate, but I had yet another aim in view.
>
> I wanted to depict in Adolphe one of the chief moral diseases of our time—the fatigue, the lack of certainty and strength, the everlasting self-analysis, which sets an *arrière pensée* beside all our feelings and so corrupts them from birth. Adolphe is clever, for cleverness to-day is within reach of all characters; he is irritable, because obstacles are a kind of galvanism which gives a moment of life to the dead; but he is incapable of a steady line, of sustained devotion, of calm generosity: his vanity alone is permanent. From child-

hood he has been nourished on the arid teachings of a blasé society; his gaiety is the wretched irony he has adopted, his rule of life his egotism. Everlastingly observing and describing himself, he thinks he has made himself superior to himself, but all he has done is to subdue his good qualities.

This disease of the soul is more common than we suppose, and many young people display the symptoms. The decrepitude of civilisation has infected them. While they think they have learned wisdom from their fathers' experience, they are merely the inheritors of their satiety. Moreover, while the older novels represented passionate men and unyielding women, the novels of to-day are full of women who yield and men who abandon them. The authors are unaware of the cause of the change. But the most mediocre and the most distinguished instinctively obey a truth they do not know.

It is not only in love-relations that this moral enfeeblement, this incapacity for enduring feeling is visible. In Nature everything is connected. Faithfulness in love is a power like religious faith, or enthusiasm for liberty. We have no power any more. We cannot love, or believe, or will. Everyone doubts the truth of what he says, smiles at the vehemence of his own affirmation, and foresees the end of what he is experiencing.

I have painted a small part of the picture, the only part which would be, not without sadness, but without danger for the artist. History will tell of the influence of this disposition of soul on other matters. For, once again, everything is connected. What makes us harsh or frivolous towards love, makes us also indifferent to any future beyond this world, and cringing towards all the authorities which succeed one another, and which we call legitimate so long as they last. Then we apply our intelligence to explain all this, and we believe that an explanation is a justification.

But the result is that heaven offers no hope, the earth no dignity, and the heart no refuge.

One of the reasons why he suppressed this is evident. It was too dangerous a thing to say in 1816, at the moment of the Bourbon restoration. And one must not suppose that Constant is merely indicting others: he is indicting himself also and linking his projection of himself into the character of Adolphe with his political behaviour during the downfall of Napoleon and the Hundred Days. That indeed was more courageous than the behaviour of most; but it was not very glorious.

The first thing to notice is that in its true context the sentence: "Not to begin such liaisons is what is wanted for happiness in life: when one has entered on that road, there is only a choice of evils" is plainly revealed as an interpolation. Again Constant is covering up his tracks. He seems to be endorsing the view of conventional morality. It is true that the careful reader even of the printed paragraph will discover that he is not. He is still incriminating society "for pouring its poisons into an affection it has not sanctioned" and endorsing the Critic's indictment.

Unhappy the woman who rests on a sentiment which everything conspires to poison, and against which society, when it is not compelled to recognise it as legitimate, arms itself with all that is bad in the human heart to discourage all that is good in it.

When, therefore, Constant says that "not

to begin such liaisons is what is wanted for
happiness in life," what he means by "happiness in life" is a condition of which he is himself contemptuous: the well-being

> Of comfortable moles, whom what they think or do
> Teaches the limit of the just and true.

The true happiness lies in a love which is
strong enough to resist the poisons which a
corrupt society pours into it. Not that he can
conceive an Adolphe capable of this: he would
need to be a changed man, who had undergone
an inward revolution. "I have shown him tormented because his love for Ellenore was
feeble; but he would have been not less tormented if he had loved her more. He suffered
through her, for lack of love; with a more passionate love he would have suffered for her."
That is true; but only of the degrees of love
that were in Adolphe's compass. Had he
loved her completely he would not have
suffered from her "false position." She had
suffered from it while she was the *maîtresse en
titre* of the Count. But that means nothing.
The spiritual datum of the story is that
Ellenore's love for Adolphe is of a totally
different kind from her affection for the Count.
It was a new dimension of experience into
which she had passed; and all she needed for
happiness within it was the assurance that
Adolphe's love for her was entire.
"His situation and Ellenore's was hope-

less," says Constant. This is true; not because of the malevolence of society, but because Adolphe was incapable of a love so entire that he could resist it. It is this incapacity which Constant proceeds to explain in the part of the preface which he suppressed.

In this he definitely and unequivocally connects and identifies Adolphe's incapacity to love with an incapacity for religious faith. "Faithfulness in love is a power like religious faith, or enthusiasm for liberty. We have no power. We cannot love, or believe, or will." I do not know whether the indictment was peculiarly true of his generation compared to those which had gone before. It certainly applies with equal force to the generations since Constant's time. That is one of the reasons for the abiding significance of *Adolphe*, and its unquestioned place among the classics of modern literature. But the important part of the declaration is its assertion of a connection between the capacity to love, the capacity to believe and the capacity to will. That connection seems to me indubitable in itself, and an understanding of it necessary to the understanding of *Adolphe*. He says it again in other words: "What makes us harsh or frivolous towards love makes us also indifferent to any future beyond this world and cringing towards all the authorities which succeed one another and which we call legitimate so long as they last." *Adolphe* does not indeed demonstrate the last, as it demonstrates the other two.  But the last follows necessarily from the truth of the others.  The incapacities have a common origin.

In order to love entirely we must believe in love, in precisely the same sense as the man of religious faith believes in God.  To believe in love is to believe it triumphant over death. This does not require a difficult exercise of the " will to believe."  It is given in the experience of love itself, by which we enter a new dimension of experience which is self-evidently external.  The experience of love is not to be confused with the experience of " falling in love."  That is only a prelude, and often an illusory one, to the gradual discovery of love through a life of mutual devotion, which is a continuous discovery, through willing self-surrender and mutual forgiveness, of an illimitable realm of freedom. We are gradually and more and more possessed by love, in precisely the same sense as the man of religious faith is gradually and more and more possessed by God. And as the self-evident "eternality" of love, dispossessing us of our " selves," comes more and more to be a matter of daily, hourly, continuous experience, so does death become apparent as a mere incident in eternal life.  It ceases to be important.  It is a finality only in one dimension of experience, and we are in daily, hourly, continuous contact with another

283

and higher one. In this sense the immortality of the soul is given in immediate and incontrovertible experience.

The love which has its most intense human manifestation in the mutual love of man and woman is a power and condition which extends far beyond this particular manifestation. It is manifest equally in the love of man for man, and woman for woman, wherever it is the motive of mutual self-surrender. It takes a political form in that reverence for the human personality which is the spiritual and moral basis of the free society. It is the only principle on which what we mean by democracy in the West can be securely founded, and by which it can endure; for that form of political society is built not on the palpable power of the majority, but on the impalpable sacrosanctity of the freedom of the minority. The saving salt of democracy is not in my belief in my own right to freedom, but my belief in the right of the other man. And what is this but love, in a less intense and more diffused form?

Love, therefore, on the one hand, as a condition entered into by mutual self-surrender of two persons united in its bond, brings men and women to the knowledge of eternal life; on the other, it seeks to establish and maintain a political society which, with all its manifold and inevitable imperfections, is congruous with itself. It ascends and descends. But it is nourished by its own transcendency. This alone gives it the power slowly and subtly to transform all human relations, yet never to be dismayed by its failure to do so. "Love never faileth." It is immune from disaster.

*Adolphe* demonstrates, or rather reveals this. It reveals it through the figure of Ellenore, and her final willing surrender to death. Through the figure of Adolphe it reveals the destruction wrought by the incapacity to love; and it reveals, as Constant truly says, the cause of this incapacity. It is an incapacity to recognise and submit to the transcendent. The marvel of his achievement is that, while depicting this incapacity in a figure projected from himself, with ruthlessness and sympathy, he at the same time revealed the transcendent in all its beauty and power.

The assurance that "love never faileth" and is immune from disaster, is the eternal essence of the Christian religion as distinct from its historical aberrations. Constant lived in a period when the empirical Christian Church was decaying—a decay which has continued ever since. He depicted in *Adolphe* the consequences not of this decay, which he did not regret, but of the decay of the belief in the transcendence of love, which he regretted bitterly, and which he felt to be the cause of his own debility. By one of those mysterious happenings which are the evidence of the power in which he could only half-believe, he was inspired to reveal its triumph.

# CHAPTER X

I find in *Adolphe* a new revelation of the
eternal truth of Christianity. I have explained
sufficiently—or at least to the best of my
capacity—what I mean by that statement as
a whole, and by the operative words within it.
When I first read the story, I expected nothing
of the kind. Nothing that I had read about
the story or about Constant himself prepared
me for this. But I found it extraordinarily
moving at the first reading, and was impelled
to translate it, mainly in order to master it as
completely as I could. It was only then that
I began to realise its full significance. The
more I realised this, the more paradoxical it
seemed that Benjamin Constant should have
written it. But when, having finished the
substance of this essay, I examined more
closely some of his other writings, the paradox
disappeared. The order of inspiration which
I claim for *Adolphe* was no longer unaccount-
able or unexpected.

I have already considered briefly, in
Chapter III, the influence which the mind, and
in particular the death, of an older woman is
said to have had upon Adolphe in his
adolescence. This older woman has been convincingly identified with Mme. de Charrière.
But Madame de Charrière did not die when
Constant was seventeen. She did not die in
fact till December 27th, 1805, when Constant

287

was over forty-one. When she died, he had not seen her for eight years, nor corresponded with her for ten, though he retained an affectionate memory of her. He was not present at her death.

But earlier in that same year,1805, he had been present at the death of a woman which moved him very deeply indeed. The death of Julie Talma did more than move him; it changed the manner of his thinking about death. Furthermore, there is no doubt that, as the critics pointed out when the *Journal Intime* was first published, the powerful description of the actual death of Ellenore in *Adolphe* is largely based on his vivid memories of the death of Julie Talma. Thus we are confronted with a striking and complicated transposition. If we take Julie Talma's death as the starting point, or original experience, it is in part transferred to the youthful Adolphe, and in greater and more significant part to the adult Adolphe.

Constant's emotional and intellectual reaction to Julie's death, as we shall see, had two phases: in the first, he was oppressed by the thought that at the approach of death the soul was disintegrating with the body; in the second, he was uplifted by the liberating thought that the soul was unaffected by the physical dissolution. " Nothing is impaired." Of these reactions only the first is transferred to the adolescent Adolphe. The portrait of

Mme. de Charrière and the account of her influence are introduced because the experience of her death had made so great an impression on Adolphe, clinching his belief that death was the end of all. The older woman and Adolphe had talked together frequently about death on that assumption, and finally: "After talking of death so much with her, I saw death strike her before my eyes." On the other hand, both reactions are transferred to the adult Adolphe at Ellenore's death. This does not imply that Constant emptied his casebook into his story. There was a complete imaginative transmutation of his material in his description of the death of Ellenore: but the psychological and spiritual substance is the same. The dying woman passes from a condition in which the disease of her body appears to the anguished friend to be destroying her soul, into one in which the soul is manifestly triumphant over the bodily disintegration; and in the soul of the observer there is a parallel change from mournful resignation to—to what? In the case of Constant at Julie's death-bed to an unexpected and unprecedented glimpse of the possibility that the soul is immortal. In the case of Adolphe at Ellenore's death-bed to something unspoken, and perhaps unspeakable.

To make this transposition still more striking, there was a close affinity, amounting almost to identity, between the ideas of Mme. de Charrière and Mme. Talma on death. Both were convinced, like the youthful Adolphe, that death was the end of all. Both were women whose friendship had meant much to Constant at very different phases of his life, and his friendship with both has been uncomplicated by passionate love. Both died in the same year. It is only a conjecture, but one cannot avoid making it, that to some extent the figures of Mme. de Charrière and Julie were blended in Constant's memory when he wrote *Adolphe*.

One other fact needs to be borne in mind. Julie died in May, 1805, Mme. de Charrière in the following December. Constant made the first attempt at *Adolphe* in the autumn of 1806. From the little that is known of this first attempt it appears to have been quite different from *Adolphe* and quite inferior to it. All we are entitled to assume is that during the autumn of 1806 his mind was working on something that was to become *Adolphe*. It was the period of " the innumerable compositions and decompositions which take place between the intellect and its thousand materials before it arrives at that trembling delicate and snail-horn perception of Beauty." Suddenly, in January, 1807, there are these consecutive entries in his *Journal Intime*:

> I am going to begin a novel which will be my history. All serious work has become impossible for me in the midst of my tormented life...
> I finished my novel in a fortnight : ....

In the commonplace meaning of the word,

certainly, we have to do with a case of " inspiration." Further, at much the same time as he
wrote *Adolphe*, he also wrote the remarkable
*Lettre sur Julie*, to commemorate his dead
friend. This letter has an intimate bearing on
the meaning of *Adolphe*.

Now for the documents. Here are the
relevant extracts from the *Journal Intime*.

> [March, 1805] Mme. Talma is dying; the
> doctors are divided, the art of medicine inadequate,
> nature inexorable. Now they tell me Blacons has
> killed himself. I could never describe the effect
> these things have upon me. . . . A year ago I wrote
> in this same journal that Mme. Talma had never
> given me anything but pleasure, and never caused
> me any pain. She is going to die!
>
> [Later] Mme. Talma is dying, there is no
> more hope. Her pretended friends are busy
> around her for the spoils. And their miserable
> calculations are disguised beneath an air of hope
> and confidence in her recovery. Her character
> is almost entirely changed by her illness. She
> is uneasy, meticulous, *miserly*. She who is so
> *generous*! Poor human nature! What is this
> soul which not only loses the means of expressing
> itself when the physical body weakens, but
> changes its tendency and almost its moral nature?
>
> [May, 1805] I dined at Mme. Talma's, who
> is dying, but more lovable than ever.
>
> [Later] I spent the day and the night with
> Mme. Talma who is near her end. I study death
> there. She has regained all her faculties: wit,
> grace, memory, gaiety, and the old vivacity in her
> opinion. Will all that be annihilated? One sees
> clearly that what she retains of her soul is merely
> vexed by the weakness of her body, but not at all
> diminished intrinsically. It is certain that if one

took that which makes her think and speak, her intelligence, in a word—all those faculties for which I have loved her so much, and transferred it all into another body, it would all revive. Nothing is impaired. Her organs are destroyed, her eyes cannot see, she breathes only with effort, she cannot lift her arm, and yet there is no damage to her intellectual part. Why should death, which is only the completion of this bodily weakness, damage it? The instrument, out of tune and half broken, leaves her inwardly what she was before. Why, when the instrument is completely broken, should it not leave this inward part intact? The spectacle of death on this occasion gives me a glimpse of ideas to which I was not inclined.

[May 8-9] She is dead. It is all over for ever! Good, sweet friend! I watched you die, I held you up for a long time. Now you exist no more. My grief was suspended by the hope of saving you once again. I contemplated death without terror, for I saw nothing violent enough to break that intelligence which I remember so vividly. *Immortality of the soul*: inexplicable mystery!

Death seems an alien power which swoops upon our poor nature and does not let go till it has strangled it. At the moment of her final crisis Mme. Talma moved as though to escape. She raised herself with force. She was quite lucid, she understood all that was suggested around her, and herself directed all the aids proposed. What then is this intelligence which was like a beaten general still giving orders to his routed army?

[Later] I have been at Mme. Talma's funeral together with a few friends who were deeply moved and affected. For a moment I feared I could not endure the mournful ceremony, doubly sad when I picture to myself the grace, the gaiety and the kindness of the woman who was shut up in the narrow coffin. The ceremony by itself was a vain pomp in which everybody performed his part, where the priests chanted psalms for payment and everything was mechanical. A queer state of things in which the very people who pretend to raise up religion and call themselves its ministers do not take the trouble to appear composed or convinced. Only one part of the ceremony seemed to me to have something touching— the salutation the priests give as they pass in front of the body, and making all the participants bless the coffin. This salutation, often repeated, is a mark of remembrance and farewell which left a tender impression on me. I had a feeling of gratitude to the men who still gave a gesture of respect to the woman who was no more.

It is evident that these bitter-sweet and vivid memories of Julie Talma's death were the material on which Constant drew for the description of the death of Ellenore. And it is possible that this was also his mental picture when he described young Adolphe's unnamed friend as dying before his eyes. Possibly, too, the memories of Mme. de Charrière and Julie merged into one another to some extent. Both had died as they had lived: women who firmly believed that death was the end of all.

But when, at end of *Adolphe*, the memories of Julie's death are drawn on for the imaginative description of the death of Ellenore, there are important differences. In the first place, although I believe that Julie contributed something to the character of Ellenore—something more essential than either Anna Lindsay or Germaine de Staël whom so many critics propose as her originals—Julie and Ellenore differ profoundly in that Julie was an unbeliever and

Ellenore deeply religious.  In the second place, the spectacle of Julie's death brought Constant to the brink of believing in the immortality of the soul: it aroused in him thoughts concerning it to which his mind had hitherto been closed.  But there is no such statement about Adolphe's reaction to the death of Ellenore.

Nevertheless, in the description of Ellenore's death Constant is faithful to both moments of his experience with the dying Julie: to the first impression that her soul was disintegrating with the dissolution of her body, and the second deeper and more abiding impression that her soul was intact, and at least capable of immortality.  But he is careful not to attribute any such thought to Adolphe himself.

Thus there is, in the death scene between Ellenore and Adolphe, a significant reversal of the situation between Julie and Constant. Ellenore is the believer, Adolphe the unbeliever; Julie was the unbeliever, Constant not indeed the believer, but one constrained at least to half-belief—one who receives a partial revelation.  This helps to explain the originating cause of the profound impression which Ellenore's death-scene makes upon the sensitive reader: as a victory of love over death.

I believe that Constant's experience at Julie's death played a very important part in the conception and creation of *Adolphe*. The thoughts beyond the reach of his soul that it aroused in him were, I think, the germ of the creation. They set the imagination at work in him; his unconscious creativity brooded upon them. Moreover, as I have already said, I suspect there is more of Julie Talma in the character of Ellenore than there is of any of the other women he loved.

In the *Lettre sur Julie* there are some indications of the kind of connection I wish to suggest between her and Ellenore.

> Julie had no religious ideas at all, and I was sometimes surprised that with her deep sensibility, her sincere enthusiasm for all that was noble and great, she never felt the need of that recourse to something supernatural which sustains us against the suffering men cause us, and consoles us for being forced to despise them; but her education, the society which had surrounded her from her early youth, her intimate friendship with the last " philosophers " of the 18th century, had made her inaccessible to all fears and all hopes of that kind. It was the one province in which she had, so to speak, abjured her habit of deciding for herself and embraced opinions ready-made. I am far from regarding unbelief as a sin; but conviction of this kind seems based on nothing, and positive affirmation in the atheist seems to me to indicate a great flaw in reasoning. Religious souls can be carried away by the needs of the imagination and the heart, and their minds may bend to these needs without being falsified; but the man who believes that logical thinking has compelled him unhesitatingly to reject every religious idea is of necessity an *esprit faux*.

Besides, Julie's unbelief was rather an impression received in childhood than a belief held on reflection; and the result was that this unbelief was lodged in a corner of her head, just as religion itself is lodged in the heads of many, without influencing in any way the rest of her ideas or her conduct. . . .

In another passage he writes:

> There is, in deep and sensitive characters, a need of the illimitable which religion alone can satisfy, and this need is so closely connected with all the lofty and delicate affections, that those who do not feel this need are almost inevitably deprived of a precious portion of feelings and ideas. Julie, however, was a remarkable exception to this rule. There was sadness in her heart and tenderness deep in her soul. If she had not lived in a country where religion had for long been a hostile and intolerant power, and its very name awoke memories of persecution and barbarity, it is possible that her imagination would have taken a quite different direction.

This is relevant for two reasons. First, because it shows that Constant regarded Julie's lack of religion as a spiritual anomaly. By her fineness of mind and her delicacy of feeling she was naturally and eminently capable of religion. Constant, who was so deeply attached to her, can hardly have avoided imagining a Julie who was religious. Secondly, because it shows that Constant held, very positively, that the man who professes atheism on rational grounds is, of necessity, an *esprit faux*. The first is pertinent to the conception of Ellenore; the second to the conception of Adolphe. Speaking roughly and approximately, we may say that Ellenore has something of a Julie to whom a belief in the Christian religion has been added; while Adolphe has even more of a Constant from whom his more than half-belief in religion has been taken away. Very possibly, Adolphe is a pretty faithful portrait of young Constant. But the point to be emphasised is that he differs in one crucial respect from the mature Constant who wrote the story. Adolphe is a person to whom it is necessary and certain that death is the end of all; his creator is a person to whom it is not, and to whom the conviction that it is is the mark of an *esprit faux*.

It is not on these grounds that I believe the idea of death is central to the imaginative drama of *Adolphe*. The impression arises directly from the story itself and had become a conviction when the *Journal Intime* was un-known to me. But the evidence of the *Journal Intime* is a valuable corroboration, and it sharpens the impression that two distinct levels of awareness were operative in the creation of *Adolphe*. These two levels of awareness can be called religious—they cer tainly are—but for reasons I have already given, I prefer to call them imaginative. On one level, death is the end of all; that is Adolphe's philosophy. On the other, there is no positive assertion that death is not the end of all, but there is a very positive conviction that the dogmatic assertion that death is the end of all is an abuse of the intellect. That is Constant's philosophy. Further, his mind had been definitely opened to the possibility of the immortality of the soul, by his experience of Julie Talma's death. I believe that *Adolphe* is the outcome in the mind of genius of months of conscious and unconscious travail originated by that experience. It became the central theme of a continuous meditation in which all Constant's experience of life was focussed— naturally and inevitably, for this is the question of questions.

The long succession of critics who have insisted that the psychological substance of *Adolphe* is an abstract and brief chronicle of Constant's relations with Mme. de Staël have done what Constant said they would do, if they were to identify its characters with individual persons. They have " degraded it, given it a false tendency, destroyed its interest and anni- hilated its usefulness." The identification of Ellenore with Germaine de Staël seems to me particularly dangerous. To identify Ellenore with any woman Constant had actually known and loved is to narrow the scope and mistake the order of his creation. That there are *traces* of Constant's experience with the de Staël, is true enough; equally there are traces of his experiences with Mme. de Charrière, Mme. Talma, and Charlotte von Hardenberg—his wife. But these experiences were only the raw materials before they had undergone the " innumerable compositions and decompositions " which Keats described as antecedent to imaginative creation. It is, at best, an unrewarding task to compare the importance of the raw materials: but if I must stand and deliver, then I would say unhesitatingly that his experience of Julie Talma's dying counted for as much in the creation of *Adolphe* as all the rest of his experiences put together.

For in *Adolphe* Constant is answering a question which he put to his own inmost soul: Whether love or death has the victory. I neither contend he did this consciously, nor admit that he did it unconsciously. In the order of artistic creation to which *Adolphe* belongs the distinction between consciousness and unconsciousness is arbitrary and precarious. But the evidence I have just set out is enough to show that during the eighteen months which preceded the writing of the story Constant was travailed by this question, and also by the kindred question whether the absence of religious belief does not betoken or create an aridity of soul. Anyone who reads carefully the *Lettre sur Julie*, in the context both of *Adolphe* and the spiritual problem which preoccupied Constant, will surely be inclined to say that it was difficult for him *not* to have tried to conceive an Ellenore—a woman in whom religious belief and devotion to a human love were one.

By imagining such a woman and by representing her as doomed to suffer unto death in her struggle to awaken love and religion in the soul of a man like himself, but with his capacity for "intimations of immortality" taken away from him, Constant lifted the fundamental question to the only plane on which a satisfying answer can be given: the plane on which it is not asserted, but can be revealed, that love has the victory. That is the revelation which is at the heart of the Christian religion. In *Adolphe* at least—and it is by far the greatest of his achievements—Constant shows himself the prophet of an undogmatic, but revealed Christianity.

A passage in the *Lettre sur Julie* bears directly on Constant's urge towards Christianity and his shrinking away from dogmas the imposition of which he felt to be intolerable. After saying that Julie was debarred, by the false bias imprinted on her mind by the *philosophes*, from considering the promises of religion as more than a means of domination and a pretext for intolerance, he continues:

> Here, I cannot refrain from reflecting on the evil done to religion and to suffering creatures who have need of it, by the spirit of domination and dogmatic intolerance. Who would not believe that, when sorrow has penetrated the inmost recesses of the soul, when death has struck us irreparable blows, when all the bonds between us and what we love seem broken—who would not

believe that a voice promising us a reunion of which we despaired, sending out from the bosom of eternal darkness an unexpected light, snatching from the grave those without whom we cannot live and whom we thought never to see again, could arouse anything but joy, gratitude, and welcome? But the comforter turns into the tyrant. He orders, he threatens, he imposes his dogma, when he should let belief sprout like a seed in the earth of hope. Reason revolts, affection is discouraged and turns in upon itself, and doubt from which we are beginning to free ourselves is reborn precisely because faith has been commanded us. It is one of the great disadvantages of religious forms, too stationary and too positive, that they inspire aversion in independent minds. They do harm to those who adopt them because they narrow and falsify their ideas; and they do harm to those who do not adopt them, because they deprive them of a rich source of comforting ideas which would make them better and happier.

Whatever one may think of this attitude, it must be admitted that it is the attitude of a man who has thought and felt deeply on the problem of religion. My sympathies, I confess, are with Constant. But the problem has changed—not indeed in its essential nature, but in the manner of its impact upon the world —in the hundred and fifty years since he wrote *Adolphe*. Since then the temporal authority of dogmatic Christianity has greatly diminished in the Western world; the nineteenth century was the century of liberalism, in religion as in other things which really depend upon religion. But the undisputed hegemony of liberalism has been brief. Europe and the world are now threatened with the recrudescence of a new dogmatic religion, infinitely less satisfying to the thoughtful and sensitive mind than the old one. Dogmatic Communism is a much more serious menace to the spirit of man than dogmatic Catholicism. For dogmatic Communism is, in origin and essence, dogmatic atheism; and, as Constant says, whereas dogmatic Catholicism does not, or at any rate need not, distort the human mind, dogmatic atheism must of necessity do so. Dogmatic Catholicism encourages, or at least permits, the human mind to be conscious of its own limitations and to move freely in the world of surmise, intuition, revelation and faith. Dogmatic atheism cuts off the mind from these vistas upon reality and avenues to truth. When it has temporal authority it invests the *esprit faux* with absolute power over human destinies. A greater disaster to the spirit of Man cannot be imagined.

The crucial political question of our age is, in the last analysis, an entirely religious one. At the first sight the problem is whether liberalism can find in itself the power and the will to resist the incessant assaults, the uninterrupted underminings of the new dogmatic religion of Communism. But it is futile to formulate it thus unless we clearly understand that liberalism can be securely based only in a religious revelation. Liberalism, whether it is aware of it or not, is not susceptible of purely rational justification. We may conceal from ourselves that its foundation is religious by calling it a moral intuition that we must respect the personality of our fellow-citizens. But there is no essential difference between a moral intuition and a religious revelation. The evident danger to liberalism is that by ceasing to be conscious that it is based on a religious revelation it may become a mere habit, incapable of defending itself with conviction against the specious dialectic of the new dogmatic religion of Communism. When the problem is seen in this light, we may begin to ask ourselves whether it may not be necessary, in order that the vague liberalism of the West shall become conscious of its own nature, that it shall return to dogmatic Christianity?

Put baldly in that form the question will appear to many a contradiction in terms. They will insist that dogmatic Christianity and liberalism are antipodal. But that is by no means so evident in the concrete as it is in the abstract. In the first place, the Papacy has now given its blessing, as a matter of religious principle, to political democracy of the Western pattern (which holds the political and religious rights of minorities to be sacrosanct), and has declared that it is a more Christian form of society than any other. In the second place, it is hardly conceivable that Roman Catholicism will be granted in the West more than the freedom which democracy grants as a matter of principle to every other religious faith. In theory Roman Catholicism may reserve its right to more, but in fact it is content with the freedom which it holds as of right in a free society. If, as I hope and some believe, a movement of rapprochement among the Christian churches is about to gather momentum, as the realisation grows that the foundations of the free society are indeed religious, and in the last analysis Christian, it can only be as a free society of Christian churches, with Rome in fact, if not in her own theory, *primus inter pares*.

Of such a free society of Christian churches, it seems to me, a mind whose faith is like Constant's could be a willing member. But a Christianity without forms and ceremonies, yes and dogmas even, seems to me chimerical. It could hardly be saved from becoming entirely amorphous. The line of advance, I believe, is not through resistance to the traditional forms and dogmas, but through accepting them more consciously as magnificent and unsurpassable efforts to express what cannot be uttered but only revealed. If a new Christianity must utter itself—as it surely must, if it is to remind itself of its own existence—then if it is truly imaginative it will be content, and thankful, to utter itself through the forms and dogmas of tradition.

I do not believe that man can remain

304

human unless he believes that love has the victory over death, or at least believes things which are apparently not so startling—such as that absolute respect must be paid to the human personality—but which have no secure foundation except in a faith in the transcendence of love. " I disagree entirely with your opinions, but I will go to my death that you may be free to utter them," said Voltaire. It was heroically said. On the vitality of that spirit the free society depends. But in order to be sure that the spirit exists in them, and that the courage is not merely verbal, men must believe that love is victorious over death. I do not believe there is any other way of making that faith accessible to all except through the Christian religion. It is the universality of the revelation that matters supremely—for the need is of a contemplation that can become common to all.

I wish to avoid misunderstanding. I do not assert that Western liberalism will be incapable of defending itself unless it returns to dogmatic Christianity, though I believe it will be unless it resolutely puts aside its secular feud with dogmatic Christianity. I am simply asserting that the non-dogmatic mind of liberalism will find no rest until it recognises that Christian dogma has ceased to be the enemy, and is now the friend. The more aware liberalism becomes of its own religious basis, the more understanding it will be of dogmatic

Christianity, and the more willing to accept
—with its own imaginative reservations—the
abiding value and humane necessity of the
traditional forms of the Christian religion.